The
Adventures of Musab

by

Fawzia Gilani

Illustrated by Rin Warrilow

Ta-Ha Publishers Ltd.
1 Wynne Road, London SW9 0BB, UK

Copyright © Fawzia Gilani

Published Rabi Ai-Awwal 1423/June 2002 by
Ta-Ha Publishers Ltd.
1Wynne Road
London SW9 0BB
Website: http://www.taha.co.uk
Email: sales@taha.co.uk

By: Fawzia Gilani
General Editor: Afsar Siddiqui
Edited by: Abdassamad Clark

British Library Cataloguing in Publication Data
Gilani, Fawzia
Adventures of Musab
I.Title

ISBN 1 842000 38 1

Typeset by: Bookwright
Website: http://www.bogvaerker.dk/Bookwright
Email: bookwright@bogvaerker.dk

Printed in England by :
Deluxe Printers,
245-a, Acton Lane,
Park Royal, London NW10 7NR
email : de-luxe@talk21.com

Contents

Musab Accept Islam

Once upon a time there was a boy called Musab, who lived with his little old mother on the edge of a great forest. Musab was a good boy and he worked very hard, but despite this he and his mother were very poor. Everyday Musab rose early and went into the forest to chop wood.

One day, while he sat and ate his bread, he saw a boy washing in the river. Then, the boy began to do unusual movements on a mat. Something about the movements affected Musab deeply. "What a wonderful but strange form of exercise!" he said to himself.

Soon it was time to go home, so Musab put away his tools and began his return journey. At home, he often sat on a white rock which overlooked the river and huge forest. There he would sit for an hour and wonder at the beauty of the sparkling water, the blueness of the sky, and the magnificence of the green forest. Then he wondered what the idols had to do with such a glorious world.

It was a sad thing indeed that Musab did not know the truth about Allah, the Lord and Creator of all things.

His mother had taught him about the idols called Lat, Hubal and Uzza. She had taught him that these idols worked with Allah and helped Him, and that you could pray to them to ask Allah to help you. And so poor Musab worshipped the idols instead of Allah. But he was always puzzled and filled with curiosity, "How could these lifeless idols to whom I pray create such a wonderful world?"

Another time, Musab happened to see the boy across the river. This time he called to him, "Hey friend! Come and share my food with me." The boy smiled and picking up his bag and mat, and made his way over to Musab. "May Allah reward you" he said.

"And may Hubal reward you" said Musab.

The two boys sat and ate and talked about different things. They enjoyed each other's company. "Tell me," said Musab finally, "Where did you learn to do those exercises on your mat?" The boy began to laugh. "Those weren't exercises," he said, "That's the way all Muslims pray to Allah." So Musab asked the boy to tell him about Allah.

"Allah is the Creator of this world." He said, "He is the One and Only and there is no one like Him. He has no children nor was He born. He gives life to all things and He gives death too."

"What does he look like?" asked Musab.

"He doesn't look like any thing," said the boy, "We just know that He is the Greatest, the most Merciful.

He hears and knows every thing. He is not like a man or like anything. But He lives forever and never dies. He is Allah, the Lord of everyone."

Musab was enchanted with the boy's words. "What about the idols we worship?" he asked "Are they not real?"

"No," said the boy, "they are things that our parents made with their own hands from wood and stone. We should not worship them, we should only worship Allah." Musab thought for a moment.Everything that the boy had told him made sense. "Teach me about Allah," said Musab." I want to worship Allah Who made the sparkling waters, the deep blue sky and the great green forest."

That day when Musab returned home, he told his mother all that he had learned. "Mother," said Musab finally, "Should we not worship Allah now, rather than the statues of Hubal, Lat and Uzza?" She smiled. "Yes my son," she said. "Today, I too accept Allah as my Lord."

And so began Musab's life in Islam. He and his mother repeated the shahadah saying, "There is no god but Allah and Muhammad is the Messenger of Allah."

Now Musab was happy. He was a Muslim obeying

and worshipping Allah Whom he had longed to know for so long.

Musab and the Thief

One day, Musab was filling water buckets from a well near his home. It was late in the evening just after Maghrib. Suddenly, a boy caught hold of him.

"Come with me," he said, "I need your help."

The boy was carrying four baskets. Musab remembered that Muslims should always help others, so he decided to go with him.

Not far from the well were four fields that belonged to a rich farmer. In each field there grew orchards, with beautiful trees bearing delicious, tasty fruit. One field had apple trees and another had peaches. The third field had oranges and the fourth had pears. The boy led Musab into the apple orchard. "Stay here and keep guard," he said, "and if you see someone watching, then quickly warn me."

The boy climbed up a tree and began to fill his basket with apples as fast as he could. Musab called out to him, "Someone is watching you." The boy stopped instantly and looked around. But he couldn't see anyone, so he kept on filling his basket until finally it was full.

The boy then went to the peach orchard. Again he climbed up and began to fill his second basket.

No sooner had he started, than Musab called out, "Someone is watching you."

The boy stopped and looked around. But he couln't see anyone, so he went back to filling his basket. When the basket was full the boy climbed down and then collected the third basket. Again, he went up a tree in the orange field and began to fill his basket as quickly as he could.

Once more Musab called up to him, "Someone is watching you."

Again the boy stopped and looked around, but he couldn't see anyone, so he carried on filling the basket until it was full.

The same happened when the boy went into the pear orchard.

Finally, he walked over to Musab and said angrily, "Why do you keep telling me someone is watching me when there is no one here?"

Musab said, "Don't you know that Allah is watching you?" The boy was full of shame. "You are right," he said. "Allah was watching me all of the time." Musab explained to the boy how wrong it is to steal and how much Allah dislikes those who commit this crime. The two boys then decided to take the fruit to the owner who was a Muslim.

"As-salamu alaikum," said Musab.

"Wa alaikum as-salam," said the farmer.

The boys explained to the farmer what they had done and asked him to forgive them. The farmer was a kind man. "Take the fruit" he said, "but in future, ask first and I will give you more, and Allah will also be pleased with you."

Musab and the Weeping Prince

One day Musab was doing wudu for Salat adh-Dhuhr, when across the river he noticed a man weeping. Musab wondered what had caused the man to be so sad.

He decided to cross the river and find out, because maybe he could do something to help.

"As-salamu alaikum, Sir, my name is Musab," he said.

The sad stranger looked up. "Wa alaikum as-salam," he replied. "I am the Prince of the Moors, the son of Hanaf."

Musab nodded, "Yes I have heard of your father, he

is a good king. I notice that you look troubled, so let us do Dhuhr together insha'Allah and maybe Allah will ease your burden."

"Insha'Allah," agreed the stranger.

After praying, the two sat down to eat. The Prince ate quietly.

"Please tell me what saddens you," said Musab. "Perhaps I may be able to help, if Allah wills."

The Prince let out a deep sigh, "I wish you could, my little brother, but I don't think anyone can help me. I weep and sorrow because I did a terrible thing. In my anger I caused a death. I forgot that a Muslim should be kind and compassionate and now I cry for my loss."

"All people make mistakes," said Musab. "Allah forgives."

"Insha'Allah, for Allah is most forgiving," said the sad Prince. "But I cannot forgive myself."

The Prince began to tell his sad story. "My companions and I would often go hunting for food. We would bring back much game that we caught with the help of my hawk, who would sit on my wrist. He was a magnificent bird and a great hunter. A few days ago, we were returning from a good hunt. I decided to take a different way home between two valleys, whilst my companions took the usual route.

The day was so hot that I began to feel thirsty. My thirst grew stronger and stronger, until finally I climbed down from my horse and began to look for a stream. In vain I searched, but I found nothing, until finally from the side of a mountain I saw **drops of water** falling. I climbed up and held out my goblet. For ages I stood with my arm stretched out watching the drops fall one by one until eventually my goblet was half full. As I took the vessel to my lips I felt a strong brush of wind and my goblet fell, spilling the water. I looked up and there was my hawk.

"Mad hawk!" I shouted in rage. "How long I waited to quench my thirst!"

I climbed down the mountain-side and picked up my goblet. Again I climbed up, positioned myself and began to collect the drops of water. When I had collected enough, I drew the cup to my lips once more. No sooner had I done this, than down flew my hawk and again knocked the goblet out of my hand.

In my anger I threatened to kill him if he came near me again.

When finally I held up the water to drink for the third time, the same thing happened again. Down flew my hawk, my goblet fell breaking in half as it crashed upon a rock.

Then I drew my sword and slew the hawk, and there it lay in a pool of blood, lifeless. With no cup to catch the drops of water I decided to climb higher hoping to find a pool at the top. The climb was difficult but, alhamdu lillah, I reached the top and there was the pool.

As I put in my hand to take a drink, I saw lying at the bottom a huge, deadly poisonous snake. And then I realised what my hawk was trying to do. Had I drunk the water I would have died. My hawk, my friend, saved my life and for his kindness I repaid him with death. And this Musab is my sorrowful story."

The Prince's eyes filled with tears. "So you see brother one should never do anything in anger for surely anger is from Shaytan."

Musab Tells the Truth

Musab had just finished praying Salat al-'Asr when his mother called to him. "Musab, we have only a little money," she said, handing him a small coin. "Please go to the village and buy a small loaf of bread, because we have no food left."

"I will do that, insha'Allah," said Musab. He was an obedient boy and always listened to his mother. "As-salamu'alai-kum," he said as he closed the door behind him.

"Wa alaikum as-salam," said his kind old mother.

Musab decided to hurry. "Maybe mother is hugry," he thought. So off he went and took a short-cut across a river. As he crossed, he slipped and the coin flew out of his hand. "O Allah!" groaned Musab. He looked for the coin, but the water was too deep.

Musab felt very sad. It was the last coin his mother had. Now he could not buy her any food. His eyes filled with tears, when he thought of his dear old mother going hungry. Musab sat on the river bank, holding his head. He did not know what to do.

Just then somebody tapped his shoulder. "As-salmu alaikum, little brother," said a stranger.

"Wa alaikum as-salam," replied Musab, trying to smile.

"You seem sad. Can I help you?" Musab explained to the kind man how he had lost the last coin he had. "Don't worry!" said the man. "Insha'Allah, maybe I can find it. I can swim well, Al-hamdu lillah."

The man jumped into the water and then dived deep down to the bottom. After a while he came up holding a golden coin. "Is this your coin?" he asked.

Musab looked at the golden coin in amazement and thought of all the wonderful things he could buy for his mother and himself. But he remembered that a Muslim who loves Allah never lies and always tells the truth.

"No." said Musab, "That is not my coin.

"The man placed the gold coin on the bank. He dived down into the river a second time. This time he appeared holding a silver coin.

"Perhaps this is your coin?" he asked.

"No." sighed Musab, "This coin is worth more than mine." The stranger placed the silver coin next to the

gold coin and then swam down a third time. This
time he came up with the missing coin.

"Al-hamdu lillah! Yes! Yes!" shouted Musab full of
joy, "That's my coin!"

The stranger smiled and placed the little old coin in
Musab's hand.

"You are a truthful boy," he said, "And Allah loves

the truthful." The man picked up the silver and gold coins and placed them in Musab's hand too.

"Here, take these coins," he said.

Musab hesitated. "Sir," he said, "I wish to get my reward from Allah." The stranger nodded, "And you

will, insha'Allah. But I give these coins to you not as a reward but as a gift. The Prophet Muhammad ﷺ asked us to accept gifts."

So Musab accepted the coins, saying, "Jazak'Allahu Khairan – may Allah reward you with something better." "Barak'Allahu fi kum – may Allah bless you," returned the stranger.

A FRIEND
LIKE THAT
MARISSA FINCH

For Abbie, who has always been the very best kind of friend —
brilliant, hilarious, and endlessly empathetic (among so many
other things.)

Thank you for always being my biggest cheerleader and my
favorite first reader.

ONE

THE LITTLE GIRL opened her eyes to darkness. She blinked against the inky black. Tried to beat it back. A bit of light peeked in from between the pale curtains that hung in the room's single window. She concentrated on the dusty slant of light painting the floor, trying to let it soothe her back to sleep.

She was thirsty. So thirsty.

She tried to stand, but there was no room. That's right. She wasn't on the bed. Not tonight. Mama had said no. Sometimes Mama said yes, but sometimes she said no. When the man came, she said no.

That meant the man was here.

The little girl closed her eyes. She could listen better when her eyes were closed. She didn't know why that was true, but it was. But even with her eyes closed, she couldn't hear anything. Maybe the man wasn't here yet, or maybe he'd already left. That meant she could get up and get a drink.

She knew how to get a drink of water all by herself now.

She knew how to push the metal chair with the scratchy red cover over to the counter. She knew how to climb up on the seat and take a plastic cup from the cupboard and hold it under the tap, how to make sure she turned the water off after. She knew how to do other things, too, like open the packages of fruit snacks or take bread out of the bag and spread it with peanut butter. She'd learned all of these things. She was good at them. Mama even said so once.

She wriggled her way out from under Mama's bed. There was just enough light coming from the crack in the curtains that she could see the small kitchen ahead. The whole house was only one room, except for the bathroom. Mama's bed took up most of the space, and a kitchen table and two chairs. A TV sat in one corner, where sometimes the little girl could watch cartoons. Only if the man wasn't here, though, and only if Mama didn't have a headache.

It would take only a few small steps to get to the kitchen chair, a few more steps to push the chair over to the sink. Then she would drink her water. Her throat smiled at the thought of it.

But she made a mistake. She looked back at the bed. She wanted to see if Mama was there, if Mama was sleeping. Instead, she saw the man.

He was sitting up. His head had tilted back so she could see the scratchy hair on his throat, the hair that went all the way down his front and disappeared under the thin sheet.

The man was asleep, because his eyes were closed. But something moved beneath the sheet. Something big and monstrous, as big as a dog, bigger, something that wriggled and bobbed.

She whimpered.

The man's head snapped up. His eyes glinted in the dark, and now she thought maybe he was the dog, maybe, and he growled, and oh God, she was so scared.

A bit of pee dribbled down her leg, hot and wet. The sheets on Mama's bed moved, and then there was Mama, her hair tangled, her orange lipstick smeared across her cheek.

"Sammie! What the hell're you doing? I told you, stay asleep."

"I was thirsty," the little girl said.

"I don't care."

"You got a kid?" the man said. His voice sounded like a monster's. The little girl shook.

"She ain't a problem." Mama stared her down, without looking once at the man beside her. "Don't worry. She's going back to sleep. Right, Sammie?"

The little girl nodded. She knew what it meant when Mama had that look in her eye. It meant business. That's what Mama always said, 'I mean business, Sammie.'

The little girl no longer felt thirsty. She walked to the bed, not to the man's side but to Mama's, laid down on her tummy, and scooted back underneath.

In the darkness of under the bed, she couldn't see Mama, or the man, and she kept her eyes open so she wouldn't be able to hear them as good. But still she heard them. It didn't matter if her eyes were open or closed. She heard them, their dog sounds. Their monster sounds.

TWO

THERE'S a check sitting on the bar top in front of me. The check is for five hundred thousand dollars. Half a million bucks. It's mine. And I can't bring myself to deposit it.

Printed at the upper-left corner, in fancy-as-shit gold embossing, are the words The Grant Hotel. That's where I work. Used to work, I guess. Where it says '*Pay to the order of*,' it's got my name. Alice Katherine Brewster. I can't make out the name of the person who signed it, but I'm pretty sure it's the CFO of The Grant. Some guy I've never met but who, judging from the ridiculously oversized signature, is either an idiot or an asshole. Maybe both. Probably both.

It's a fancy check, one where the paper looks like fake marble, and there's a pale holographic G in the middle. Security feature, I guess, but it also adds to the ostentatious, untouchable feeling of the thing. It's not so fancy anymore, though, because every day I come in here, to a dive bar called El Diablo, and I sit at this bar and order a drink, and I put the check down in front of me. So I can see it. So I can stare at it.

It's crumpled and soft from coming in and out of my pocket too many times, and there are water stains and a ring of red wine from where I accidentally set my glass down on it one time. God knows what else.

I probably shouldn't be carrying it around with me every day. I definitely shouldn't be leaving it out on the bar. But like I said, I can't bring myself to do anything else with it just yet.

Why? So many reasons. Mostly because I don't want it to be real.

Monica, the bartender on duty, sidles over to me. "Another drink?" she asks sourly. Monica is my least favorite of all the bartenders who sling drinks at El Diablo, but she works on Thursday afternoons, and today is Thursday afternoon, so there you go.

"Yes." I jut my chin out and push my empty glass toward her, right over the check. One more stain won't hurt.

"Coming right up," Monica says, still sour, even though I'm ordering drinks and spending money and no one could accuse me of loitering.

Then again, maybe she's not actually sour. Maybe I'm just projecting. I've never been good with other women. Not that I'm good with men, either. I guess you could say I'm a misanthrope.

Monica deposits my drink in front of me. Gin and tonic today. I like to mix it up. Mondays are tequila sunrises. An easy, citrusy start to the week. Tuesdays are white wine, Wednesdays are red. Thursdays, I start on the hard liquor. Friday is straight up tequila shots. I don't come on the weekends, because I don't need to. My mother expects me home on the weekends, so that's where I am. At our little house on Staten Island. My childhood prison. I mean home. All the same, really.

I squeeze the wedge of lime over the glass and drop it in, using the tiny blue straw to stab at it a few times. I should have asked for extra lime, but Monica probably would have forgotten, anyway. Accidentally on purpose. I take a sip, but I can barely taste the gin.

If today were a normal day, before all this happened, I'd be at work. At The Grant Hotel. My first — and it seems, only — job. I loved that job. I was a housekeeper, so it was hardly glamorous work, making beds and washing strangers' hair out of showers, but I loved coming into the city every day, putting on my uniform, earning a paycheck. But things haven't been normal for a while now, so instead of being at work or at home, I'm at a dive bar in downtown Manhattan, sipping juniper spirits under the watchful eye of the almighty Monica. Fucking cheers to me.

The door of the bar swings open, and I squint against the sunlight. It's a perfect fall day out there, the kind where you can imagine couples strolling through Central Park holding hands and wearing matching plaid scarves. That kind of vomitus stuff. But inside El Diablo, the lights are dim and red-hued — that's part of their schtick, El Diablo, like the devil, get it? — and everyone, at least at this time of day, sits alone. Though we're never really alone, are we? None of us. No matter where you go, your thoughts and memories and dreams are always with you, beating like a second heart. One that pumps poison instead of blood.

I'm sorry, was that overdramatic?

Anyway, the front door slams shut behind the latest

patron. It does that if you aren't careful. The regulars know to let the door ease closed behind them, but newcomers always jump when the thing slams shut. It can be quite comical, actually.

This time, the newcomer — a woman maybe my age, with blonde hair — doesn't flinch at the sound. She heads straight for the bar and sinks onto a stool a couple away from me, letting out a deep and exhausted sigh as she does. She flags Monica down right away, but hesitates before ordering. She glances around, as if looking for inspiration. When she spots my drink, she points to it.

"Gin and tonic," she says. "Extra lime."

"Coming right up."

As soon as Monica turns away, the blonde whips out her phone. Typical. Yet another millennial who can't go five minutes without telling the world where they are and what they're doing. I'm a millennial, too, technically, but I wasn't allowed a phone until I was almost out of high school, so I never got in the habit. Plus, I have no friends and no social life, so the whole social media thing is kinda lost on me. See above re: misanthrope.

But even though I find myself feeling judgmental and angry — my default states — I watch the blonde. I suppose it's because she's just got that kind of face. That kind of energy, if you want to be all new age about it. Some people just have it, you know? That kind of energy you can't look away from. It's compelling in a way that average people aren't.

If you want to be less new age about it, it could also be that she's straight up beautiful. And I say that as a straight woman. A misanthropic straight woman, at that. She's blonde, which is the first thing working in her favor. I'm technically blonde, too, but mine leans toward the mousy shade, while hers is the color of warm honey, and laced through with expensive-looking highlights. She's blue-eyed, too — another tick in her favor, and one up on me, since my own eyes are brown. It's hard to say how tall she is, since she's sitting down, but I'd guess about my height. So maybe five feet six. Perfectly average, though that's the only thing about her I'd describe that way. Her figure is definitely not average — more the knock-out type, if I'm being honest. Hourglass. I'm what they call boyish. Polite magazine talk for 'no boobs and no ass.' I've always appreciated my slim, straight build — at twenty-five, I can still fit into the Peter Pan costume I wore when I was twelve — but looking at the blonde next to me, I feel something that seems to me like a pang of envy.

I look away. *Eyes on your own paper, Alice.* It must be the gin. I don't know whether I should drink faster or slower, so I opt for faster. I knock back the rest of my drink, and when Monica returns with the blonde's cocktail, I nod at my own empty glass. She rolls her eyes, or at least I assume she does. I'm already sneaking more glances at the blonde.

She's put her phone away and is studying the glass in front of her. Almost like she's steeling herself for something. She picks up the drink, swivels toward me, and says, "Cheers to getting hammered on a Thursday afternoon."

I never smile, but I smile at those words. "I'll drink to that." I lift my empty glass. "Or I would if I could."

"I'll drink for both of us." She drains her glass in two solid, impressive gulps. When Monica returns with my G&T, the blonde nods at her own empty glass.

Monica throws her hands up in the air. "Could you two at least get on the same schedule? Or are you trying to outdo each other?"

My bar-mate snickers. "Just keep them coming, okay?"

Monica turns away, irritated, and the blonde leans over to whisper conspiratorially. "If you drink that fast enough, I think we can really send her over the edge."

I bite back another rare smile, but I only sip at my drink. I've already had three, and if I throw this one back on top of the others, I'm going to be too drunk even for me. I prefer drinking just enough to take the edge off things — all those thoughts and memories and dreams, beating away inside me, that second poisonous heart — but not enough that I'm completely out of it.

With her fresh drink in front of her, the blonde leans over again. "A proper cheers this time." She holds her glass up, and I clink mine against it. Even though it's loud in the bar, with the rowdy conversations and the thrum of old Pearl Jam songs playing on the speakers — the sound of our two glasses clinking together reverberates through me. It rings in my ears long after I've taken a swallow and set my drink back down on the green and white Heineken coaster.

"I'm Taylor," she says as she angles her body toward me. "And I'm an alcoholic."

"I'm Alice," I say. "And I'm..." I try to decide how to finish that sentence. What am I? If I knew the answer to that, I probably wouldn't be at a dive bar getting wasted on a Thursday afternoon. I let the thought trail off.

"Oh God," Taylor says, covering her mouth. "I was only

kidding about that. About being an alcoholic. You're not... are you offended?"

Offended? No. It takes more than that to offend me. But I *am* slightly perturbed by her attention. I don't come to El Diablo to make friends. In fact, I come here because it's one of the least friendly places I can think of. The people in here, like me, are not exactly joiners. No one comes here to have a conversation or to make a connection. We come here to drink, to dwell. Occasionally to dine, if we're feeling particularly brave and steel-stomached.

Taylor, bless her heart, is oblivious to all this. She's staring at me expectantly, waiting patiently for me to play my part in the conversation game. And the longer I take, the more she looks worried that she really did offend me.

"I'm not offended," I say. A peace offering. I gesture around the room. "Add a box of donuts and this could be an AA meeting."

"Except for all the drinking," she says, happy to be playing the game again.

"Except for all the drinking," I agree.

"So what's fueling your alcoholism?" Taylor asks. "Family? Boss? Boyfriend?"

I think about how to answer that, but Taylor is already speeding ahead without me. "Me, it's my roommate. She's practicing for an audition and seriously, if I have to hear the monologue from *A Streetcar Named Desire* one more time, I'm going to slit my own wrists. 'He was a boy, just a boy, when I was a very young girl.'" She groans in exaggeration. Or at least I assume it's exaggeration. Who knows? Maybe she really is on the verge of slitting her wrists. "What about you?"

"Same," I say after some consideration.

Taylor laughs. She has one of those loud, unapologetic laughs. Men sitting in the back of the bar look up and take notice. It's rare that a woman as beautiful as Taylor graces this place, and she's got their attention now, whether she likes it or not. But she's oblivious to their stares; I imagine she's used to them.

"I like you, Alice," she says. She slides over onto the seat right next to me, closing the distance between us.

I flush a little. I'm not sure if it's because of the compliment or her nearness. I'm embarrassed by how much I like both of them. I've never been a joiner; even at work, when I was surrounded by other women my age, I didn't make a single friend. Not really, unless you count Minnie, the shift supervisor, who was more of a kindly aunt than a friend. Maybe that's why when *the thing* happened, I kind of lost myself. No one had my back.

And now what do I have? A five-hundred-thousand-dollar check I can't bring myself to cash. My eyes drift to the stained scrap of paper in front of me. Taylor notices, and her gaze follows mine.

"Whoa!" She picks it up. "What is this?"

"A check."

"I know but, like, is it real?"

"It's real."

"Alice Brewster," she reads. "Five hundred thousand dollars. Jesus, woman. This is baller money. What'd you do?

Oooh — is this, like, one of those egg donation things? Can I do it, too?"

"It wasn't an egg donation thing." I pluck the check from between her fingers. Even though I've been careless with it, I don't like the idea of anyone else holding it. "And no, you probably don't want to do it, too."

"It's dated over a month ago." She squints at me. "Why haven't you deposited it?"

I shrug. I don't want to look at her anymore. I stuff the check into my pocket, where it should have been. I regret leaving it out on the bar. That was stupid. Not because it could have been stolen or damaged — I obviously don't care about that — but because of this. Someone seeing it and asking questions I'm not comfortable answering. If I don't come to El Diablo to make friends, I definitely don't come here to talk about *the thing*.

"Alice Brewster," she admonishes, as if we've known each other far longer than ten minutes. "You need to deposit that check. Before you lose it."

"What if I don't want to?"

"Why wouldn't you want to?"

I shrug again. It's a gesture I'm very good at. My bony shoulders move up toward my ears so easily, it's like they're magnetized.

But Taylor is unfazed. "Look, if you don't want that money — though I don't know why you wouldn't, do you know what you could do with five hundred thousand dollars? — there are plenty of ways to put it to good use. You could donate it, for instance."

"To who? To you?"

"No." Taylor looks as sour as Monica did when she was mixing our drinks. "How about animal shelters? Women's shelters? Homeless shelters?"

"Animals, women, the homeless, oh my," I say, mockingly. But her words get me thinking. Maybe donating the money *would* be a good idea. The weight of it would finally be off me and my poor bony shoulders. The money could help someone who needed it, instead of someone who never wanted it, aka me. I drum my fingers on the bar top.

"I'm right," Taylor pronounces. "You know it. Come on. It's four thirty. Most banks are open for another half-hour. I'll go with you."

Even while I'm slurping up the last of my gin and tonic, I know I'm going to take Taylor up on her offer. I don't know why I'm letting this stranger talk me into something I haven't been able to talk myself into for weeks, but I won't argue with fate. The thought of finally being free of this check is spurring me to action. And if it took a strange blonde woman and a few too many cocktails to get there, so be it.

"All right," I say eventually. "Let's do it."

Taylor grins. The gesture comes as easily to her as shrugging does for me. "Atta girl. Come on — I'll even pay for the drinks." She flags Monica down, produces a credit card, and two minutes later, we're pushing through the door of the bar and out into the crisp sunshine beyond.

THREE

"WHERE'S YOUR BANK?" Taylor asks, pushing her blonde hair back out of her face as the wind makes every effort to return it again.

"Seventh and West 49th."

Taylor spins in a circle to orient herself, then points. "This way."

I let her lead the way. I barely know her, but I can already tell that's how it is with Taylor. It doesn't matter who you are or where you're going — if you're with her, she's leading the way. That's the charisma again. The energy. I find myself with no choice but to follow her.

The bank is several long blocks away, and we hoof it so that we can get there before five. I don't know why it doesn't occur to me to get a cab or an Uber. Habit, I guess. Theoretically money isn't an issue for me anymore, but it's hard to shake twenty-five years of conditioning. Cabs are a splurge, and we don't splurge in my house.

Taylor and I get to Wells Fargo ten minutes before it

closes. There aren't any other customers there, so one of the tellers — there are three of them, idling against their stations and chatting, running down the minutes until closing — waves us right on over.

I breathlessly present her with the check. After hanging onto it for so long, it's weirdly exhilarating to be finally doing something with it. And something good, at that.

She takes the check without a word, but when she spies the amount on it, she frowns. She glances back up at me, her penciled-in eyebrows receding up into her hairline. Her frown deepens as she considers me. Probably wondering how a hundred-pound, malnourished mouse reeking of gin and wearing a Ramones t-shirt got her hands on five hundred grand. Can't say I blame her on that one.

"I'm going to need to get my manager," she huffs.

Clearly, I've put a dent in her plans to get out of here early. She disappears and returns a minute later with a portly man wearing a blue tie stained with something. Coffee, I'm going to hope. He looks at the check and at me, much as our teller did. Except he also looks at Taylor for a few long minutes, too.

"We'll need your bank card," he says, and I produce it from the wallet I keep in my back pocket. The card sticks when I try to pull it out — the wallet is still so new that the stiff leather makes everything difficult. I say a silent RIP to my last wallet, which was worn soft and perfectly molded to the shape of my ass, but got stolen from my locker at work one day, not that long before *the thing*. Apparently *nothing* good happens at The Grant.

Taylor hovers next to me as I go through the motions of

inserting the card into the machine and entering my PIN. I stand there feeling like a criminal while they stare at my information on the screen.

"All right," the bank manager says eventually. "We'll deposit it for you, but because of the amount, there's going to be a five-day hold on the funds."

"No, she needs that money today," Taylor interjects before I can respond.

"I'm afraid that's out of the question."

"She's donating it."

"That's all well and good, but it has no bearing on our process. We need to verify the check with the issuing bank. Once the funds have cleared, you'll be able to access your money. We can grant you a maximum of five thousand, if that'll do. That's the daily withdrawal cap on your account, Miss—" he checks the computer screen again, "—Brewster."

"No, it won't do," Taylor says.

"It'll do." I step in front of her. Now that I'm here and I'm doing this, I want it done. "Five thousand is fine for now."

A few minutes later, I'm holding five thousand dollars cash in my hand, and the data from my check is zooming somewhere around the digital banking world, waiting to return to me someday soon.

"That was bullshit," Taylor says as we emerge back into the crisp fall air. "I'm sorry. I feel like I got your hopes up for nothing."

"It wasn't nothing," I say. It's true. Depositing that check, and having at least a vague idea of how to use the money, has been an enormous weight off my shoulders. One that might not have ever lifted, were it not for Taylor. That's definitely not nothing. Staring down West 39th, with the sun sinking and casting the concrete in a warm golden glow, I feel lighter than I have in weeks. Definitely since *the thing*.

"Okay, so now what do you want to do with it?"

"I guess we find a charity." I spin around. I actually have no idea where to find one out here, surrounded by banks and offices and fast food and all the other trappings of capitalism.

But Taylor's already whipping out her phone. "What are you thinking? Homeless shelter? Animals? Veterans?"

"What about sexual assault?"

"Sexual assault?"

"Like... survivors. Or domestic abuse, maybe."

"Okay, yeah, good. Let me see." She taps a few buttons on her phone and scrolls for a bit. "Here's one that's not too far. The New York City Alliance Against Sexual Assault. Over on Broadway."

"Let's get a cab." After all, now I have five thousand dollars to blow.

But when we get to the listed address, we find the doors locked. We bang on the glass, but no one appears.

"I'm sorry," Taylor says. She sounds as defeated as I feel. "I thought there'd be someone here. I guess it's not an actual shelter. It must be just an office or something."

"That's okay. I'll write them a check as soon as I have my money."

Taylor and I both lean against the exterior of the building. The stone is freezing cold against my back. What must it be like to be homeless in this city; to have nowhere to put your ass but on the sidewalk or curled up in concrete vestibules like this one?

I jump up and head back onto the sidewalk. "I have an idea."

Taylor follows me. "Where are we going?"

I don't answer her, but it doesn't take long to find what we're looking for.

In an alley two blocks away, we see a homeless man in a dark coat, sitting pensively on a flattened piece of cardboard. He's got a winter hat pulled low over his forehead, so that his eyes are barely visible. There's another hat on the cardboard in front of him. He isn't specifically begging for change, but I figure he won't turn it down, either.

"Hello, sir," I say. I fish five hundred-dollar bills out of my pocket and drop them into the hat. "Have a nice day."

He nods once, but otherwise barely acknowledges the money. Maybe he hasn't noticed how much it is. That's okay. I don't need any recognition. I just want to be free of it.

We give another five hundred to a woman pushing a shopping cart loaded down with garbage bags stuffed full of recyclable cans, and some to a young guy with a leather jacket, camo pants, and a pit bull. We put a thousand in the Salvation Army donation bin, and when we duck into a coffee shop to warm up for a few minutes, we stick another few hundred-dollar bills in the donation box on the counter — something for a kids' summer camp — and another two hundred in the tip jar. We exit the store before they notice, in a burst of breathless laughter.

It feels good to be doing something with the money. For so long, it's hung over me like a pall, and now, I'm finally breathing fresh air again.

"Where to next?" I ask Taylor, who seems to be enjoying this as much as I am.

She looks at the time on her phone. "Shit. I can't. Sorry, Alice. I'm supposed to be meeting some friends for dinner."

I look at my own phone and realize it's past seven o'clock, and I have half a dozen missed calls. I usually head home right around five, the same time my hotel shift used to end. My mother will be worried. Panicked, actually. It's kind of her thing. "Shit. Me, too, actually." I hesitate. Suddenly, I really don't want to go home. I don't want to face my mother and that oppressive house. I don't want to walk back into the pall. I like it out here. In the fresh air.

Taylor hesitates, too. She tucks a strand of blonde hair behind her ear. "Is it weird to ask if you want to get dinner sometime? As friends, I mean. I'm not trying to hit on you. It's just that... it's hard to make friends as an adult, right?"

"It is," I say. I'm smiling again. Who am I, even? "It totally is. And yes, I'd love to have dinner and no, it's not weird."

"Great. Why don't you give me your number? I'll text you."

She hands me her phone, and I type in my number. I'm the first name in her contact list — one of the benefits of having a name that starts with A. I secretly hope that means she'll see my name often and be more likely to actually call, and then feel like a total loser for even having such a thought.

I pass the phone back to her, and for a second Taylor looks like she might hug me, but backs off. Just as well. I'm not a hugger. And even though I like Taylor, I'm not ready to go there yet. Instead, she gives me a wave and hails a cab. As she's about to get in, I stop her.

"Wait. Take this." I press the rest of the cash into her hands. She stares down at it in shock. It's a little over a thousand dollars.

"Alice, I can't."

"I insist."

"I—"

"No, really. I insist. And it's not a bribe or anything. It's just... thanks for making my day suck less."

She smiles. "Ditto."

Ditto, I hum to myself as I walk to the closest subway station. *Ditto*.

I should wonder why it is that I feel so comfortable with Taylor. Why it is that I — decidedly not a joiner — am so enamored with a stranger I met at a bar.

I should, but I don't.

FOUR

BY THE TIME I get home, my mother has worked herself
into complete hysterics. She's about ten minutes away from
calling the police. I know this because she screams it at me as
I drop my bag and plod to the kitchen for a glass of water.

"Where were you?"

I can measure her level of anxiety by the octave of her
voice, and right now she's somewhere in the middle C range.
Not good.

"I'm sorry. Work ran late." My mother doesn't actually
know that I no longer have my job at The Grant. That's why
I go to the bar every day, so that I don't have to tell her the
truth.

"And you couldn't call?"

"I'm not allowed to have my phone on me when I'm on
shift. It was in my locker, and I didn't have time to go down
and get it. They had a bunch of dignitaries coming in, and the
rooms needed to be cleaned ASAP." The first part, at least, is
true. We weren't supposed to keep our phones with us when

we cleaned. Supposedly, the rule ensured the guests' privacy, but the real reason is management didn't want us dicking around on Facebook when we were supposed to be working.

Not that my mother needs to know any of that.

"Dignitaries?" she says, alert now. Interested. "Who?"

"Oh, I don't know. Some Turkish diplomats, I think."

"Oh." Her shoulders droop. Probably hoping it was someone from the Royal Family. My mother has a bizarre obsession with them. Mostly she hates celebrity culture, but she can name every function Kate and Meghan have ever attended, and probably what they wore, too. "Well, next time try to call. I didn't know what had happened to you. I thought there could have been an accident, you could have been hurt—"

"Do I look hurt?" I snap.

My gut twists as soon as I say it. I know I shouldn't be mad at her. She can't help that she's the way she is, and God knows I've had an entire lifetime to get used to it. She has severe and crippling anxiety, and that's just a fact of life. I used to think it was down to my father. Anyone would have severe and crippling anxiety living with him; look how I turned out. But he's been dead almost ten years, and she's gotten worse instead of better. It's left her unable to leave the house, unable to handle even the most basic life tasks. A shell of the person she used to be.

But I guess that's what happens when you kill your husband.

I know — kind of a shocker. Imagine how I felt when it happened.

And to be fair, I don't know *for sure* that she killed him.

It's just a gut feeling I've had since it happened. It always seemed a little too coincidental that he died in a random mugging only a few weeks after she told me she was going to 'do something about this, once and for all.'

At the time, my naïve sixteen-year-old self thought that meant we were finally going to leave him, move in with my Aunt Barbara in Colorado the way Mom had been threatening for years. Then Dad got shot, twice in the gut, in the alley beside his favorite pub. The one he went to almost every night, the one Mom was always nagging him about because he spent so much money there and always came home drunk off his ass. He had bled out there in the alley, like an animal. At the hospital, I overheard a nurse say that he must have suffered; that it had taken him over two hours to die.

I wanted to pity him. I wanted to hate my mother for what she'd done. But I didn't. I couldn't. My father had terrorized both of us. He had a temper as thin as a knife blade, and a drinking problem that sharpened that blade to a razor's edge. My mother bore the brunt of his physical anger, though we both got our share of tirades, put-downs, and bullying. He was a hateful man, to put it plainly. And Mom felt stuck.

So I guess she did the only thing she thought she could.

I never told anyone my suspicions. Not the police, not Enid, my best friend at the time. I've never even brought them up with Mom. What am I going to say? *Hey, by the way, did you kill Dad?*

Instead, I keep my silence. And I help my mother. The shopping, the banking, all the paperwork that her anxiety keeps her from being able to deal with. I'd tried to get her to file a disability claim, but she won't even go see a doctor to get an official diagnosis. It's not the stigma of the condition that concerns her; it's the literal act of leaving the house that's so overwhelming. I can count on one hand the number of times she's been outside since Dad died.

That's why I had to get a job in the first place, a fact that she hates. My father had a basic life insurance policy. That was a shocker, actually; I expected him to screw us over in death as much as he had in life. But the policy was small, and even though we lived frugally, we burned through it in about five years, especially after Mom insisted on using a good chunk of it to pay my college tuition. So I went in search of a job. Four years at the College of Staten Island, and the only work I could get was cleaning up after entitled guests at The Grant.

And now I don't even have that. Is it any wonder I want to keep that fact away from my mother?

I drain my glass of water and hunt in the cupboards for something to make for dinner. It's been a while since I hit the grocery store, so the pickings are slim. I find a box of pasta and a jar of red sauce, but there's nary a vegetable in sight. I feel guilty feeding my mother the equivalent of a toddler diet, even though I know she won't complain. Now that I have the proceeds of that check sitting in my bank account, I'll use some of it to buy her better groceries — organic vegetables and free-range meats and hormone-free dairy and all that other stuff. The best of the best.

Except now that I'm home, away from Taylor, the thought of spending that money seems repugnant again.

Somehow, with her, it had felt freeing and fun. A way to unburden myself. Now it feels the way it did before — like I'm taking hush money. Like I'm putting a price on my dignity.

Which, I guess, is exactly what I'm doing. My silence is worth five hundred thousand dollars. It says so right on the non-disclosure agreement they made me sign. In triplicate.

I want to go upstairs and take a long, hot shower. I've learned, over the last month, that there isn't a shower hot enough to scald away the shame, but still it's the only thing that brings any relief at all. But my mother is standing there watching me, and I guess she's probably hungry and I feel guilty for worrying her and making her wait, so I grab a pot and fill it with water.

I stand at the stove and wait for the water to boil, which means it takes ten times longer than it should. As the tiny, simmering bubbles turn into big, boiling ones, I wonder if this water might be hot enough to scald away the shame. I imagine plunging my hand right into the pot, letting the water burn me, purify me. The urge makes my muscles twitch, and my hand clenches.

I stare at the bubbling liquid for so long that my mother says, "Alice?" from somewhere behind me. I shake my head and dump in the dried pasta noodles.

"Sorry, Mom. Just zoned out there for a second."

"Are you sure you're all right?"

"I'm fine."

"I worry, you know."

Of course you do, I want to say. That's the whole problem. But I keep that thought to myself and instead stir the pasta so it doesn't stick to the bottom of the pot. The urge to stick my hand in the boiling water has passed. It was so strong it scared me. Where does a thought like that come from? And why is it so hard to resist?

My mother and I eat dinner at the small table in the kitchen. In silence. There's no more mention of my late return, no questions about my job, not even any comment on the sad state of our meal. It's how I like it. If I could, I'd take my plate up to my room and eat in solitude.

When we're done, my mother disappears into the living room to watch *Jeopardy* while I clean up. My father hated that show. He was terrible at trivia — probably because all the alcohol rotted away the memory-storing parts of his brain — and he thought Mom was showing off when she watched it. She learned to never blurt out answers if she knew them; too many correct ones in a row would lead to a backhand across the face. It was such a treat when Dad would be away on business and Mom and I could watch the show in peace. It blew me away how smart she was; how she could have done anything she wanted with her life, except that instead she'd trapped herself here with him. With *us*.

I hand wash the dishes in the sink. I wanted to get Mom a dishwasher for her birthday last year, but the thought of having someone into the house to install it was more than she could handle. While I wipe the remnants of dinner from our plates, I let myself daydream about the life I might have someday. In this future, imaginary life, my mother doesn't have any issues. She lives independently, without my help. Actually, in the daydream, I'm never specific about where exactly she is. She's alive, for sure, because sometimes we meet for lunch or go to a museum together, or I take her shopping. But she doesn't live with me, and she doesn't need me to do things for her. She can leave the house by herself; she has her own life.

In the fantasy, I live in Manhattan. I have a studio apartment, because I'm at least semi-realistic, even in my fantasies, and I know there's no way I'll ever be able to afford more than that. I probably won't even be able to afford a studio, let's be honest, but I need something to strive for. So. A studio apartment in Manhattan. I don't work at The Grant, but at some hip little gallery or coffee shop. Wait, no, that's too much contact with people. Maybe this time I'll be a hip graphic designer. But not the kind who sells out to work for big brands. I'll be the kind who works with artists, bands, the off-off-off-Broadway shows. I ride the subway to work, instead of the ferry, and I drink overpriced coffee. I have a cat. A few plants. A vintage record player.

In the fantasy, of course, *the thing* never happened. In fact, in the fantasy, I never took that job at The Grant. In the fantasy, I went to New York University after my father died, then got an artsy job in the city. I didn't have a mother to take care of, a life to put back together.

From the kitchen table, my phone chirps. Could it be Taylor? Maybe her dinner wrapped up early and she wants to do something. Something fun, something you can only do in Manhattan. She'll ask if I want to come downtown. I'll have to say no, of course, but for a second I let myself think maybe I wouldn't. Maybe I'd just go.

There's no point to the speculation, though, because

when I pick up the phone I realize it isn't Taylor at all but my friend Enid.

Okay, *friend* might be a stretch. Or at least a term that's outlived its usefulness. Enid lives next door to us. We were best friends in elementary school, but drifted a bit in high school. Another thing I can blame my father for. Having friends isn't easy when you're trying to hide the truth of what's going on in your own home.

Enid and I got a bit closer when we both ended up going to the same college. She seemed so happy about it, too. She'd show up here every morning, a book bag on her back and a stupidly large grin on her face. But it didn't last. After we graduated — a sad little ceremony that I had literally no one to invite to and only went because Enid insisted — I started working downtown at The Grant. Enid stayed home and started a podcast and we just sort of... fell out of touch. Sometimes I feel guilty about it, but at the end of the day, I don't know if the fact that we're the only two people from our graduating class who haven't moved away or gotten married already is enough to sustain a friendship.

I read Enid's message: **"Want to come over and watch a movie?"**

I almost ask what movie, but there isn't an answer she could give that would make me want to say yes.

"Sorry," I type back. **"Long day at work. Rain check?"**

"Sure. Tomorrow?"

I sigh. I don't really want to commit to something tomorrow night either, but I still find it incredibly hard to say no to Enid. There's something about her that's so... simple. I don't mean that in a bitchy way, like she's slow or something. Just that her friendship — her needs and her tastes and her expectations — are all so uncomplicated. She has a podcast about eighties pop culture, so all she ever wants to do is chill in her mom's basement, watch movies, and eat homemade snacks. It's nice, actually. Kind of reminds me of the simpler days before my dad died. Before *the thing*.

I should spend more time with her, I chide myself. Friends like Enid are good to have.

"Sounds good," I type, after only a moment of hesitation.

That night I spend half the night checking my phone, waiting for a text message. Not from Enid, but from Taylor. I know that it's stupid to think she'll text so soon. Even to think she might text at all. Maybe she was just being polite, feeling sorry for the weird lonely girl she met at the bar. Not that I'm lonely, but I can see how I might have appeared that way to a stranger. So that must be it — she felt sorry for me, so she asked for my number. No way she's going to text.

Still, I pick up my phone every five minutes, looking for something that isn't there. I guess it's because, for the first time in ages, I've spent my day — or at least a large swath of it — thinking of something other than *the thing*. I can't remember the last time that happened.

The next day, Friday, I park my butt in my usual spot in front of the bar at El Diablo. This time, instead of just drinking and generally being misanthropic, my eyes dart back and forth between my phone and the door. I know it's pathetic, but I'm still waiting to hear from Taylor. I even entertain the fantasy that she might walk through the door again, that we could have some sort of adventure, a distraction from spending another long afternoon pretending I still work at The Grant.

But she doesn't appear. Doesn't text, either. Eventually, I pay my tab, ride the subway down to the ferry terminal, and head back to the island.

My mother and I eat another silent dinner. I've already told her I'm going to Enid's for the evening. Though she worries when I'm out of the house for too long, she doesn't mind when I go to the Connollys'. I guess she feels safer knowing they're literally within shouting distance.

After I've cleared the dishes, I go upstairs to freshen up. When I've changed my t-shirt and brushed my teeth, I grab my phone. One new message. Expecting something from Enid — probably a request for snacks — I open it without thinking.

"It's Taylor," the message says. **"I got 2 tix to The Diviners at Lee's Hall 2nite. Interested?"**

Hell yes, I'm interested.

But I can't. I've already agreed to hang out with Enid tonight. Plus, some of the girls I used to work with at The Grant liked to go dancing at Lee's Hall, and so I already know it's definitely not my scene. It's the kind of bar where girls wear false eyelashes and guys pop their collars, and it's all a bit much if you ask me.

Although the answer is obvious, I stand there in my bedroom, staring at the phone, paralyzed with indecision.

Despite all the reasons to say no, something tells me to say yes. Something tells me to do something fun for once in my damn life, to take a chance.

Before I can change my mind, I type a reply to Taylor. **"I can be downtown in an hour."**

Someday my tombstone will read *Alice Brewster: Always Was An Asshole*, but right now, I don't care. Taylor represents an escape, a chance at a life more thrilling — less suffocating — than this one, and I'm taking it.

FIVE

THE FIRST THING I do is text Enid and tell her I'm not feeling well. She replies with a string of sad-faced emojis and then has the gall to ask if I want her to bring me soup or ginger ale. I beg off her kindness, feeling like the world's largest piece of human shit.

I go downstairs and feed the same line to my mother. I consider letting her think I'm still going to Enid's, but I don't know how late I'll be, and I don't want her worrying. Easier to tell her I'm sick and sneak out the way I used to. She'll sleep better thinking I'm snug in bed.

But as soon as I say the word 'sick,' her face turns green.

"Do you think the chicken was bad?" She presses her hands to her stomach, as if she's already experiencing the effects of some imaginary salmonella.

"No, no, nothing like that. I think I probably caught a bug at work. I'm going to lie down. I'll probably fall asleep, so if you don't see me again tonight, don't worry."

"Okay." She already looks worried. "Let me know if you

need anything. I can make you a lemon honey tea if you want."

"Maybe later. But probably not," I add, in case she gets the idea to pop her head into my room to check on me. "I think I just need sleep."

"All right. Feel better." She plants a kiss on my forehead and ushers me back upstairs.

Once I've closed my bedroom door, I consider changing my outfit, but ultimately decide against it. I already know Lee's Hall isn't my style, and I have nothing suitable to wear even if I tried to embrace it. Jeans, tee, and leather jacket it is. The only concession I make is to trade in my combat boots for a pair of black and white sneakers. Easier to climb in.

I unlock the bedroom window and silently slide it open. Right below my bedroom is the roof of our kitchen. It's part of an add-on that's not original to the house. My parents had refitted it to a kitchen almost twenty years ago, when I was little. Dad had made a big production about giving Mom her dream kitchen. Why work all those long hours, he said, why spend all that time on the road, if not to be able to give his girls everything they could want. The first night after it was finished, Mom cooked steaks for her and Dad — chicken fingers for me — and Mom had overdone the meat slightly. Dad had backhanded her across the face. It was the first time I saw him hit her. I was five.

Next to the kitchen is a large oak tree. It stretches almost as tall as the house, and one of the largest branches protrudes right up over the kitchen. From my bedroom, it's an easy hop out onto the lower roof, a quick scale down the tree. From there, I can cut through the neighbor's yard and emerge on the street directly behind ours.

I step silently onto the roof, then slide the bedroom window closed behind me. I use the branch to climb closer to the trunk of the tree, where the branches are more numerous and the climbing is easier. When I'm there, I pause and slip out my pocket knife.

I know I could give up the ritual, but I've been doing it so long that it's almost ingrained. I use the knife to score a small line in the tree bark. There's one line for every time I've used this tree to sneak out of the house. Probably a few hundred of them. I call it my getaway tree, but these are marks of cowardice. When my parents were fighting, I'd use this tree to get out of the house. Instead of trying to help my mother, I'd spend hours walking around. Walk until I was so cold or so tired that I had no choice but to come home. By then they'd usually be asleep, or at least the raging would have stopped. In the morning, there'd be my mother's bruises to contend with, my father's hangover, but at least for a few precious hours I could sleep.

When I've finished making the mark, I slide the knife back into my pocket. The knife, ironically, came courtesy of my father. It wasn't a gift, nothing touching like that. I'd stolen it from him one night when he'd been passed out. I was scared he'd use it on Mom, or on me, so I slipped it out of his pocket and hid it in my room. I let him think he'd lost it at the bar. It's the one thing I don't feel guilty about.

I shimmy down the tree and drop silently onto the grass below, emerging onto the street behind ours and walking downhill toward the ferry terminal.

It takes me forever to get to Lower Manhattan — thank you, Staten Island Ferry — and by the time I get there, I have another message from Taylor.

"Lee's was a bust. :(Hitting up Karnival. Find me there."

I don't know if Karnival is the actual spelling or a result of clumsy typing. I search for it online, but can't find anything. Scratch that — I find no references for the K-spelling and way too many references for the more traditional C-spelling. Neither helps me.

"Address?" I message. I'm not nearly cool enough for this.

A minute later Taylor drops me a location pin. I hail a cab.

When I arrive, I'm expecting to find a club, with a line of scantily dressed women and douche-y guys wending its way around the corner. Instead, all I find is a deserted warehouse. The only clue that there's something going on behind the thick cinder block exterior is the dull throb of bass pulsing through the night air.

I look around for an entrance but can't find one. There's no signage anywhere, and nothing that even resembles a door. I check the address on my phone again, but as far as I can tell, I'm in the right place.

I walk around the side of the building, where an alley stretches into the darkness. Nope, not going down there. I may not be a true city girl, but I'm from Staten Island, and I definitely know better than to walk down a dark alley at night.

I'm about to turn around and go back to the street, where I plan to try texting Taylor again, when I hear something. I freeze. It comes from the alley, a hissing sound. A stray cat, maybe. I try to catch my breath. It's just a cat. Stop being such a wuss.

The sound comes again, but this time I realize it's more of a "*pssst*" than a hiss.

I squint into the long alley and make out a dark shape I hadn't noticed before. A hunched, vaguely human sort of shape. I turn back to the street, ready to get the hell out of there. The vaguely human shape speaks.

"Want to take a ride?" The voice is eerie, both childlike and sinister at the same time.

My heart skips a beat. He's talking to me. But what the heck is he talking about? *Want to take a ride?* Hell no, I don't want to take a ride.

Suddenly, I want to be back home, hanging out in Enid's basement, eating her mom's homemade chocolate chip cookies and laughing off her older brother Heath's cheesy jokes. I want to be watching eighties movies and gushing about how underrated *Heathers* is. I want to be... anywhere but here.

For the first time, I think about how well I know Taylor. Which is to say... I don't. And yet, on her invitation, I've found myself in a dark and deserted alley, with nothing but an almost-dead phone. No one even knows where I am.

"Take a ride... if you dare," the figure says again. He's closer now, close enough that I can see it's a man. He's short

— not quite a dwarf, but shorter than me by at least a head. He looks even shorter because he's all hunched over. He's wearing what appears to be some kind of burlap robe, and his head is cue-ball-bald.

"Excuse me?" I say. My voice cracks. Fear tightens the back of my neck.

"A circus of delights awaits you," he says. He grins at me, and there's something so deformed about that smile that I shudder. He keeps coming toward me, hobbling along, dragging one foot behind him slightly. I let out a tiny shriek.

He laughs, and there's something in the sound of it that makes me take a closer look at him. He's wearing make-up, I realize. And on his wrist, an expensive watch. His words circle in my mind. *A circus of delights.*

"Karnival," I say. My voice cracks, still hoarse with my earlier fear.

"But of course," he says with a flourish. "Step right up, step right up." He waves his hand at me and starts walking back down the alley, gesturing for me to follow.

Half of my instincts are warning me to stay out here on the main street where at least there are lights and other people and cabs whizzing by. But the other half are urging me to follow him. I wanted a life with more experiences, didn't I? Besides, Taylor's already in there. What could go wrong?

I'm smart enough to know how many situations have gone awry after someone uttered those exact words, but that doesn't stop me from stepping into the darkness after him.

The pseudo-hunchback leads me to the end of the alley where he opens a door that I never would have found on my own. It's the same stone as the building exterior, and it blends in so seamlessly that it's virtually invisible to the naked eye. All part of the experience, I guess.

As he pulls the door open, the music gets louder. The thumping bass becomes an all-out blast of sound. As soon as I step inside, he lets the door swing shut behind me, and I'm surrounded by music and lights and madness.

Because that's what this place is — madness. Long swaths of red fabric hang from the center of the high ceiling and drape out toward the sides, giving the illusion that we're inside a giant circus tent. Performers of all stripes mingle through the crowd. I pay an exorbitant cover charge to a magician who disappears my money into a top hat, while a ticket taker on stilts bends over gracefully to stamp my hand. Aerial artists swing overhead on gleaming silver rings. In the center of the room, a crowd throbs and flows on the dance floor.

I have no idea how I'm going to find Taylor. I take out my phone and send her a text telling her I'm here, but there's no response. My phone is almost dead and I pray it'll hold out at least until I find her. I push my way through the crowd. A waitress with hot pink pigtails and a tiger-print bodysuit glides by, holding aloft a tray of shot glasses filled with a glowing purple liquid. I take one and throw it back. It fizzes inside my mouth. I almost spit it back out.

"Pop Rocks," the waitress shouts, laughing when she sees my expression. "You know, the candy?"

I force it down. It's like drinking a grape-flavored electrical shock. I keep pressing through the crowd, trying to find Taylor, but there are too many bodies, too many faces, too many flashing lights and pulsing bass lines.

I grab my phone to try texting her again, but she's already replied. I hadn't felt or heard the buzz over all the other sensations going on. Her message indicates she's at the bar, so I head that way.

SIX

AT FIRST I don't see Taylor anywhere, but then her blonde head comes into view, illuminated under a bright yellow light, making her glow golden. I have the sudden and ridiculous thought that she looks like an angel. She laughs at something and sips a drink from an oversized martini glass, and even from here I can see her eyelashes fluttering, mostly because they're twice the size of any normal person's lashes. She's talking to a guy in a shiny royal blue blazer, slicked back blond hair. They look like they belong together, or at least that they're part of a matching set. Razzle Dazzle Barbie and Club Kid Ken. Everything about him is plastic. I instantly hate him.

I sidle up to Taylor, but it takes a minute for her to notice me. In fact, it's the Ken doll who notices me first. When his eyes keep drifting up over Taylor's shoulder, she eventually turns around to see what he's looking at — *what could possibly be more enthralling than her,* I think somewhat bitterly.

But as soon as she sees me, her face lights up. She flings her long, slim arms around me and squeezes me in a hug that's stronger than I'm expecting. I hug her back, even though I'm normally not a hugger. For some reason, with Taylor, or maybe in this strange bar so far removed from reality, hugging is acceptable.

"You made it," she half-squeals, half-shrieks. "What took you so long?"

"Sorry. I had to come all the way from Staten Island."

Taylor wrinkles her nose, making it clear what she thinks of that, but she laughs again. "I never would have pegged you as an island girl."

"That's me," I say, and then don't know what else to say.

"You don't have a drink," Taylor proclaims. She turns back to the bar. It takes all of one and a half seconds for the bartender — a man about our age, with a handlebar mustache so comically oversized that it probably has its own zip code — to saunter over, despite the crowd at the bar. Taylor orders something with a name I don't recognize, and when it arrives, it's pink and served in the same style oversized martini glass Taylor's holding.

"Cheers to our continuing alcoholism," Taylor says, tapping her glass against mine. The Ken doll from earlier is forgotten. I spot his blue blazer disappearing into the throng of people on the dance floor. I imagine a dejected stoop to his shoulders, but that's probably wishful thinking.

I sip my drink, and am surprised to find that it's incredibly delicious. Not too sweet and not too sour and not too boozy and with a hint of a flavor I can't pin down.

"Good, right?" Taylor beams. "The Starlet. It's my own invention. Gin, cranberry, and a splash of hibiscus juice."

"It's incredible."

"Yay! I'm glad you like it." She drains her own glass. "Want to dance?"

"Dance?" Hell no, I don't want to dance. I eye the throbbing crowd with equal parts suspicion and revulsion.

"Come on, it'll be fun."

No way does grinding up against a bunch of strangers constitute my idea of fun, but Taylor looks so hopeful and excited that, somehow, I find myself being led into the center of the room, holding my drink up over my head so it doesn't get knocked about.

On the dance floor, I sway awkwardly to the pounding music, but Taylor — Taylor is magnificent. I know that sounds super corny, but I don't know how else to describe it. She looks like she was born to do this. Her eyelids go to half-mast, and her arms spin lazy but graceful circles in the air. Her hips move on their own schedule, making luxurious figure-eights that I could never manage with my own cinder block pelvis. Her long blonde hair tumbles down over her shoulders, changing colors as the lights sweep over us — blue, then green, then purple, then pink. Her silver dress picks up the same colors, but in sparkling highlights that twinkle like stars.

Lest you think I'm paying too much attention to her, I should mention that *everyone* in the bar is staring at Taylor. She's objectively captivating, and I'm clearly not the only one who feels that way. The good thing is that with all eyes on Taylor, no one is paying attention to the nobody beside her. I try to match her movements, uncoordinated and ox-like, frumpy in my black jeans and leather jacket, but at least no one is watching.

While we dance, I slip my phone out of my pocket. Its death is imminent, but I quickly open the camera app and snap a covert picture of Taylor. I try to capture something of her etherealness under these colored lights, but before I can look at the picture, the phone dies completely. I stuff it back in my pocket before she can notice.

I make it through about three songs — at least, I think it's three songs. The DJ makes everything blend together — before I finish my drink and beg off back to the sidelines. Taylor tags along.

"Are you having fun?" she shouts when we're back at the bar.

"Yeah," I answer, then grimace. "Sorry, no. Not really."

She laughs, throwing her head back so her long white throat is exposed. "I like you, Alice."

"Thanks." I'm embarrassed to admit that a light heat creeps into my cheeks.

"Do you want to get out of here?" she asks. "It's dead in here tonight, anyway."

Dead? In here? I look around at the pulsating crowd in disbelief. I don't argue, though. I'm glad to get the hell out. "Let's go."

We push our way toward the exit. All eyes seem to follow us. No, not us. Taylor. An overwhelming sense of relief comes over me when we burst into the same dark alley I'd entered through. But instead of heading toward the street, Taylor turns the other way.

"Come on," she says. "I know a shortcut."

I hesitate for only a moment before following her down the alley.

We've walked only a couple of minutes, but it's enough for the throb of the bar's bass line to have faded away to almost nothing. The only noise from here is the distant hum of traffic, the sound of a siren somewhere.

Then, a groan.

I glance at Taylor, but she's stopped moving. There's another sound. More high-pitched this time. A whine, almost. And a voice.

"Don't. Stop."

Another whimper. Taylor grabs my hand, but instead of pulling me back toward the street, we go deeper into the alley, in the direction of the noises. A sick bubbling fills my stomach.

"Hey!"

Taylor's voice beside my ear is as loud as a gunshot. My head reverberates with it. She lets go of my hand, and then she's running forward. I see where she's going a moment before she reaches it. It's a couple, pressed up against the brick wall of a building. They're shrouded in darkness, but even still, I can tell he's holding her hands up above her head, pinning them to the wall. Restraining her. His other hand is fumbling under her skirt.

My stomach heaves. Darkness hoods my vision. Images of *the thing* dance behind my eyelids. I need to lean against something, but I'm standing in the middle of the alley and there's nothing to lean on.

In that girl's face is an expression of pain, of fear. But also of resignation. She knows no one's going to save her, that this man is going to get his way, because don't they always?

"Oh, hell no." Taylor's voice is like another gunshot beside my ear.

Before I realize what's happening, she's flung herself at the man, arms flailing and fists clenched.

SEVEN

TAYLOR FLIES AT THE MAN, fists waving. She slugs him in the back, in the neck. He turns, and she cuffs the side of his head. He grunts something unintelligible. The girl he'd been attacking is screaming, a constant high-pitched wail.

The man lunges at Taylor, pawing at her, trying to grasp her arm.

"Taylor, watch out!" I yell. I want to help, but I'm frozen to the spot. It's not just fear; in my mind, *the thing* is flashing, white hot sparks clouding my vision.

Taylor ducks, avoiding the guy's grasp. When she comes back up, she grabs the lid off a metal garbage can. She swings it at the man, clocking him hard in the back of the head. He goes down heavier than a sack of trash.

For a minute, everything in the alley is quiet. Bile rises in my throat. The shrieking starts again. This time with actual words.

"Oh my God, Johnny!" The girl in the skirt drops to her knees, cradling the head of the man in front of her. She stares up at Taylor in horror. "You crazy bitch! What did you do? You killed him! You killed my boyfriend."

Boyfriend? Killed? We—

The bile that had started to rise in my throat explodes, and I turn around to puke into a dumpster. The grape-flavored Pop Rock shot tastes the same coming up as it did going down.

"He's not dead," Taylor retorts. "He's clearly breathing. And I was helping you, you ungrateful bitch."

The wave of dizziness passes. Not dead. Not dead. Thank God. But when I turn back around, I can't tell. The guy — Johnny — is on the ground, flat on his back. Blood pools beneath his skull. He's not moving. The girl clutches his t-shirt. Her nails, painted pale blue, are long and talon-like. "Johnny, oh Johnny," she mewls.

My stomach bottoms out. Is he really—

But then, a groan. Clearly coming from the guy on the ground. I let out a wobbly breath.

The girl is fishing around in her purse, and when she produces a phone, she waves it at Taylor. "I'm calling the police, you psycho."

I freeze, and for a second, so does Taylor. We stare at each other. I tried to read what's in her eyes, but they're inscrutable.

Her face breaks into a grin. "Run!"

She tears off down the alley, back the way we came from, her heels clattering on the asphalt. I hesitate for a second, casting one glance down at the poor girl on the ground, cradling her boyfriend's head with one hand, the other hand fumbling with her phone.

"Sorry," I mutter, right before I take off after Taylor.

By the time I catch up with her, she's reached the street. Unlike me, she doesn't appear to be completely out of breath. Her arm is up, hailing a cab.

"Better to call an Uber or something," I pant. "Won't it take forever to get a cab here?"

She smirks as a familiar yellow sedan careens to a stop in front of us. "Not when you look like me."

Fair enough. I climb into the backseat beside her.

It's not until the cab is a couple of blocks away from Karnival and that damn alley that I can finally breathe again. When I glance over at Taylor, she's studying me. I flash her a tentative smile, and her face breaks into a delighted grin.

"That was crazy," she gasps, cackling. "Oh my God."

"So crazy," I agree. I try to laugh, but nothing about what just happened feels funny. "Do you think he's going to be okay? Maybe we should have stuck around."

"He's fine," she declares. "I could see right away that he was breathing. I didn't even hit him that hard."

I don't say anything. My entire body is trembling. Maybe Taylor can tell that I'm on edge, because she shakes her head.

"My God," she says again, twisting her hands together. "I thought he was, you know, hurting her... I thought she didn't want..." She lets the thought trail off.

"I know. So did I." I taste sour grape in the back of my throat again. I close my eyes against *the thing*.

"Good, so it wasn't just me." Taylor sits back. "I couldn't stand it. Thinking that he was hurting her. I had to do something." She looks at me imploringly, as if that last statement isn't a statement at all, but a question that she definitely needs me to agree to.

I do. "You did the right thing," I assure her. *And you did it when I couldn't,* I want to add. I'm the one who tries to look so tough, and yet you, in your stupidly high heels and your sequined dress, are the one who took charge. "We had no way of knowing that was her boyfriend. It really looked like he was..."

"It did. It totally did." She leans back against the seat and closes her eyes. I try to do the same, but every time I do, a rolling anxiety courses through me.

Eventually, the driver pulls to a stop in front of a mid-sized apartment complex. Taylor starts to get out, but I stay in my seat.

"Come on," she says, reaching for my hand.

I shake my head. "No. Sorry. I've got to get home."

"You've already missed the last ferry."

"Shit, really?" I grab my phone from my pocket, but remember it's dead.

"Yes, really. You can either pay for a cab, which is expensive, or try for a late bus, which is a pain in the ass. Or you can crash at my place."

She's still holding out her hand, so I don't give it any more thought. Even though I could easily afford the cab ride, and the bus isn't actually all that bad, I slip my hand into hers and let her lead me up to her apartment.

Taylor's apartment is not what I'm expecting. Then again, I don't know *what* I was expecting. The walls are painted beige, and the sofa in the living room is big and brown. A painting hangs behind it — a bland, abstract landscape in blues and greys and taupes. A glass coffee table and a large TV on a matching glass stand complete the room.

Taylor gestures to the couch, and I sink gratefully into it. I realize, as I take in the brown coasters on the coffee table, the small decorative glass jar filled with smooth, grey stones, what's wrong with the apartment. It's *bland.* Nothing about Taylor is bland to me, yet this apartment could belong to anyone in the world. It's practically a hotel room, it's so impersonal.

Taylor sees me eyeing the space. "Yeah, I know." She shrugs. "This is all my roommate's stuff. She's very... beige."

Right. The roommate. "Is she here?" I ask, keeping my voice low.

"Nah. She's at her boyfriend's. She spends most of her time there."

"That must be nice."

"It's perfect." Taylor grins. "I just wish she'd go ahead and move in there completely so that I could redecorate. Hey, I'd even need a new roommate." She lets that thought settle for a second and then asks, "Want a drink?"

I still taste grape flavored bile in the back of my throat, but the idea of a drink to steady my nerves sounds appealing. "Whiskey, if you've got it."

"I think so. Sit tight."

Taylor turns to the kitchen, which, as in most city apartments, consists of a small galley space that's half open to the main living and dining area. She opens and closes cupboards, and I hear the clinking of glassware as she runs the faucet. A minute later, she returns to the living room with two tumblers, still wet from washing, and a large bottle of whiskey, two-thirds full.

"Here." She hands them to me and shrugs on a hoodie that's draped on the back of the sofa. It looks too big for her and completely out of place with the sparkly silver dress she's wearing. "My roommate's," she explains again, with an easy shrug. "Come on."

"Where are we going?"

"Just follow me."

She doesn't bother locking the apartment door behind her, which feels both cavalier and weirdly brave. We take the elevator up to the top floor of her building, which looks identical to Taylor's floor, and climb a dim set of stairs up to a heavy steel security door. The words FIRE EXIT are emblazoned on it in red. Taylor leans on the handle, and it opens. Cool air blasts my face. We're on the roof.

"It's the only place in the whole building that isn't totally stifling," she explains.

We walk over to a couple of patio chairs, clearly already there for exactly this purpose, and Taylor flops into one. I have no idea what part of the city we're in. We'd been in the cab for about twenty minutes, but I didn't pay too much attention to where we were headed. But up here, the Manhattan skyline is laid out in glorious splendor. The Empire State Building, One World Trade Center, the Chrysler Building. It's New York City perfection.

"Wow," I say, because I'm cool and articulate like that.

But Taylor grins. "I know, right?"

There's a glugging noise, and Taylor holds out a whiskey glass that's very generously filled. I take it, and she grins as she pours one for herself, equally full. "Cheers," she says.

We clink glasses for the second time that night, but I'm much happier here than I was at Karnival. The night sky, the fresh air — even though it's colder than a witch's tit — the view of the city sprawled out before us. Karnival felt oppressive, but I can really breathe up here.

I sink into the chair across from Taylor and take a long sip of the whiskey. The burn hits just right, and I close my eyes in bliss.

"You're funny," Taylor says and sips from her own glass. "I'm glad I met you."

"Likewise."

Meeting Taylor is the only good thing that's happened to me since... well, since I got my job at The Grant, I guess. Although, look how that turned out. Landing that job had seemed like a godsend at the time, but it turned out to be the worst thing that ever happened to me. So Taylor's got a leg up in that regard.

Unless, of course, she turns out to be the next worst thing that ever happened to me. I think again of the guy in the alley, the blood pooling under his head. I picture the wild animal glint in her eye.

But looking at her now, her blonde hair tumbling down over her shoulders, her oversized hoodie dwarfing her narrow shoulders, her legs hitched up underneath her to stay warm — well, it's hard to see how that could be the case.

"What do you do?" I ask, out of the blue. I flush slightly. "I just mean... I barely know anything about you."

"There's not much to know. I'm an actress. Well, trying to be. I work at a coffee shop most of the time, which is fine but, you know, it's not really what I want. Someday I'm going to go out to California."

"California?"

"If you want to be an actress, that's the place to be. New York's fine if you want to do stage or whatever, but I have a face that's meant for the big screen, don't you think?"

Instead of answering, I take a swallow of whiskey. California. So far away.

"Wouldn't it be hard to leave? I can't imagine going so far away from the place I grew up. From my mother." Even in my fantasies of moving out of my mother's house and starting a brand-new life, I never venture that far from home. Manhattan is more than far enough for me.

"Well, you're lucky," she says, with a clear note of bitterness in her voice. "Not all of us had perfect childhoods. I couldn't get away from Ithaca fast enough." She shakes her head as something catches in her voice, something I don't recognize. Something I've never heard from her before. "I thought New York would be far enough away, but ... no, California is the place for me." Her confident smile is back.

"Why are you still here, then?"

This causes Taylor's bottom lip to jut out slightly. "Because it takes money to start over. Do you know how expensive LA is? I'm not exactly rolling in it, as you can see. Someday I'll get there, though. Someday I'll just pack my bags and..." She walks her fingers lightly away from her, as if indicating floating away.

"I have money," I blurt. I don't know why I say it. I want to help Taylor, but not if helping her means that she's going to leave.

She laughs. "I'm not taking your money."

"But maybe—"

"No. Alice, no. I'm not taking your money. I'm not a charity case."

"I didn't say you were. I just..."

"End of discussion."

Fine. I take another long swallow of whiskey, and another, and another. We lapse into a silence that's not exactly comfortable but is at least companionable.

"So, about that money you got..." Taylor starts. "Do you want to talk about it?"

I sigh and take another sip from my glass. "Not really."

"That's cool." She's staring up at the sky, not looking at me. "I just don't think I've ever known anyone to get a check for a half a million dollars before."

"Yeah, well. It wasn't exactly something I wanted."

"I got that impression."

I don't say anything else, and we lapse into silence again. A shooting star goes by. I realize that tears have pooled in my eyes. I blink furiously. I don't want them to fall. I don't want Taylor to see them.

"I worked at this hotel," I say. "The Grant."

"I've heard of it. It's kind of fancy, right?"

"Fancy? Yeah, I guess so. They get a lot of high-end

guests. Lots of dignitaries, politicians, CEOs. People who think they can do whatever they want."

Taylor laughs. It's a deep throaty laugh, the kind you always associate with cool girls. The kind of girls who probably smoked cigarettes in high school and knew how to give blowjobs without ever once practicing on a banana in the privacy of their bedroom closet. Not that I've done that, mind you.

"I bet they left you some interesting things to clean," she says, grinning. "Shit in the showers? Sperm on the curtains?"

"There were a few incidents," I say carefully. We're getting dangerously close to *the thing*. And that's something I haven't talked to anyone about.

"So how come you don't work there anymore?"

Maybe it's because we're not facing each other, because we're each staring up at the sky. Maybe it's because I hardly know Taylor, and that makes it less scary. Maybe it's just because she might understand.

"I was raped," I tell her.

EIGHT

I WAS RAPED. It's the first time I've said those words out loud. Most people say *assaulted* these days, or sometimes *sexually assaulted.* Rape has become a word that's scary to hear. Even scarier to say. Just the sound of it hollows out the pit of my stomach. *Rape.* It's such an ugly, violent word, for an ugly, violent act.

Taylor sits up straight and stares over at me. I can't look at her, but I feel her eyes on me.

"Alice, shit. That's horrible. I'm so sorry."

When her hand touches my arm, I startle. A single tear trails down my cheek, and I brush it away with the sleeve of my jacket.

"I'm not really supposed to talk about it. At least according to the non-disclosure agreement I signed, anyway."

"Fuck the NDA," she spits. "That's bullshit. You have to talk about these things. That's how you heal, you know."

I don't know about healing. I don't know if that's even

possible. Even after more than a month, *the thing* still sits inside me like a black hole. Like it's carved out the space where all my vital organs used to live. Like it's the only thing alive inside of me anymore.

"Well, whenever you want to talk about it, I'm here."

"It was my own fault," I blurt. "We were supposed to clean that guest's room in twos. That was the rule. I didn't really know why, but... whatever. I guess we sort of knew, but no one ever came out and said it. They just said we were to go two to the room when he was there. They pretended it was so that we could go faster, that the guest liked his privacy and didn't appreciate the cleaning staff in there for any longer than necessary. But that wasn't the real reason. I know that now. Hindsight, right?" I flash her a rueful grin that's far more self-possessed than I actually feel. What I feel is like the human equivalent of a raw, open wound.

"Who was it?" Her voice sounds far away. Or maybe she's whispering.

"No one you've ever heard of. This guy from Texas. Weston Chambers." It's the first time I've said the name out loud since *the thing*. No — the rape. "He's the son of this oil baron or something. I don't know. I think he's some kind of real estate developer now."

Taylor doesn't respond. It's as if she's waiting for me to go on. And for the first time, I find I actually *want* to go on. Ironically, it's the NDA that's making me want to talk. It feels like at least a small 'fuck you' to the hotel, which hung me out to dry. As if money could make up for what they knew would happen to me. *Did* happen to me.

"Anyway, he was staying at the hotel that week. He came every month or so. I was scheduled to clean the room with another girl. Camila. She was nice. Super reliable. But she got a call that day. The school. Her kid had been in a fight or something. She was going to wait till we were done, but I told her to go, that I'd be fine."

Now that I'm talking, the words don't stop coming.

"I know I should have got someone else to come do the room with me, but I figured it would take as much time to find someone as it would to do it myself. We were always on tight timelines there. Between us, we had hundreds of rooms to do every day. There wasn't time to waste. If you fell behind, the whole schedule got out of whack.

"Besides, I'd done it by myself before. The last time he came, the girl I was working with got food poisoning at lunch. She was puking in the locker room all afternoon, waiting for her husband to come in from Jersey to pick her up. I cleaned the whole room myself, and it was fine. I never even saw Weston Chambers. I figured I could do it again, no problem."

The words fall from my mouth at a frantic pace, as if I'm desperate for Taylor to hear them. To understand all the thinking that went into this, all the decisions I made that led up to *the thing*.

"At first, it was fine. He wasn't even there. I moved through the room at lightning speed. Stripping the sheets, cleaning the shower, wiping down the sink. I was almost done when he got back. I was fluffing out the curtains. So stupid, right? Fluffing the fucking curtains. But we were supposed to do that in every room. Pull them open if they were closed, and give them a good fluff and shake, to make them look full and get any dust out. I heard the door unlock behind me. I knew it was him."

"Damn." Taylor takes a small sip of her whiskey, but her eyes never leave my face. "So close."

"I know. If it wasn't for those curtains..."

"Damn," she says again.

"Yeah. Anyway, it happened fast after that. He looked around, realized we were alone in the room. I tried to leave, but he blocked my way. He... well, anyway, it happened. He tried to throw a couple of hundred-dollar bills at me on my way out, but I didn't take them. I guess you could say I was waiting for an even bigger payout." I smile bitterly.

I hadn't wanted *any* payout. I'd gone to the hotel HR department to report what had happened because I wanted... I don't know what I wanted. For them to call the police? So there'd be an investigation? Newspapers, media, scandal? I wasn't thinking about all of that, or I might not have gone at all. I guess all I'd wanted was a little compassion.

Instead, I got blame. I'd known the rules, they said. The room was to be cleaned by two people at a time. They couldn't be held accountable when I was the one who had broken the rules.

I suppose they were trying to intimidate me. I sat in that pristine office with Diane Cantwell, the head of HR, and a prissy little bald man who I think was one of the hotel's lawyers, and I'm quite sure that even they saw their bullshit for what it was. Diane kept looking at the ceiling, at her stapler, at the bald man beside her — anywhere but at me.

But they had to make me feel like shit first, to ensure I'd take the deal. So that I'd agree to their lousy NDA and their payoff. It worked, too. By the time I left that office — broken and sore and devastated — I'd have signed anything they put in front of me. In some ways, it was worse than the rape itself.

Some ways. Not all ways, though.

"Weston Chambers," Taylor says. Her face twists in anger. "I hate him already."

"Me, too." It feels good to say it out loud. *I hate him.* I hate his stupid over-the-top accent and his striped shirts and his blond goatee and his ridiculous belt buckle. I hate everything about him. I hate even the thought of him, that even though he's half a country away, he's *out there.* Just living his life, free of any consequences or even remorse.

"I wish he'd drop dead," I admit. "Or better yet, die some horrible, gruesome death. One where he has just enough time for a come-to-Jesus moment, where he realizes what a complete and total piece of shit he is."

Not much chance of that, though. Assholes almost never realize they're assholes. Not even at the very end. We're all the heroes of our own lives.

"That would be epic," Taylor says, leaning back in her chair and grinning. She takes another sip of whiskey. "Maybe we should kill him ourselves."

"Ha." I drink. "That would be some poetic justice, wouldn't it?"

"I'm serious," Taylor leans forward. "He doesn't deserve to be alive. If the hotel had a rule about him, it's because he's done this before. People like that — there's no helping them.

They think they deserve whatever they want. That they can just take, take, take. You can't reform them. They're broken on the inside. The only thing to do is remove them from the face of the earth."

I expect Taylor to be grinning, but her face is dead serious. I laugh. It's the only appropriate reaction under the circumstances, right? I laugh. "Sure, Taylor. Let's do it. Let's kill him."

"You think I'm joking, but I'm not."

"Okay," I say, but inside I'm still laughing. The idea is too absurd, especially coming from blonde, bubbly Taylor.

"It probably wouldn't be that hard," she muses, leaning back in her chair. "If he had enough privacy to assault you, there'd be enough privacy to kill him. We could do it right at the hotel. How's that for poetic justice?"

"Perfect. We break into his room and... what? Shoot him? I think someone would notice."

"Of course they'd notice if we shot him," she says, rolling her eyes. "But there are other ways to kill people, you know. Quieter ways."

"Right. So... we stab him?"

She shrugs. "That would work. And it would be kind of appropriate, don't you think? He essentially did the same to you. He just didn't use a knife. But tell me it didn't feel exactly like you were dying when it was happening. Like he was cutting you open, bleeding you dry. Stabbing him would be karmic retribution."

"But with more blood," I joke, though I realize as soon as I say it that the joke hits a sour note. Neither of us laughs. I sip my whiskey. "Anyway, I'm not even allowed into The Grant anymore. That was part of the agreement I signed."

I say it as if that settles things, as if some contractual clause is the real reason we can't kill Weston Chambers. But the idea still hovers between us, as dark and dangerous as a loaded gun.

We don't talk about Weston Chambers for the rest of the night. We talk about nothing at all, really, even though we stay up on the roof for another couple of hours, until we're both shivering and the whiskey's all gone. By the time we go back down to Taylor's apartment, I'm exhausted and more than a little drunk. I fall asleep on her couch as soon as my head hits the squishy brown cushion.

The next day, I pay for my troubles. A raging headache accompanies me all the way back to Staten Island. Taylor, on the other hand, had appeared no worse for wear, looking perky in a pair of pink silk pajama shorts and a tank top. As she handed me a couple of Advil and a bottle of water and waved me off, she looked downright cheerful.

The ferry ride gurgles my stomach, and when I hit dry land, I splurge on a cab up the hill to my house. I have the driver park one street over, so that I can sneak back into my bedroom via the getaway tree. If all goes well, my mother will have no idea that I spent the night anywhere but snug in my own bed. And I can pass my hangover off as a lingering effect of whatever mystery illness had laid me up last night.

It's a little risky, cutting through our backyard in the full light of morning, but there's no movement through the kitchen window. I scale the tree a little more slowly than usual, but it's still easy enough to make it to the small roof outside my bedroom window. I slide the sill up and prepare to slip inside, when something makes me freeze.

There's someone in my bedroom. And it's not my mother.

NINE

THE FIGURE STANDING in my bedroom turns around slowly. I try to duck down below the window, but I'm not fast enough. The shadowed figure lets out an ear-splitting shriek.

I *know* that shriek. I pop my head up again and gesture frantically for her to be quiet. When Enid realizes it's me, she stops screaming and runs to the window.

"Oh my God, Alice, we thought you were dead," she snaps as she slides the window the rest of the way open.

I climb in. "Not dead. Just stayed in the city last night. What are you doing here? Is my mother awake?" The last is a stupid question; after Enid's scream, there's no way anyone within half a block is still asleep.

"Awake? Of course she's awake. She's been awake all night. We all have."

Enid's already pale skin is even more color-deprived than usual. Her dark red hair, which is normally pulled back into a neat French braid, is frazzled and unruly. She's wearing a rumpled pink t-shirt with a unicorn on it, slim-cut burgundy jeans, pale yellow slip-on sneakers. In other words, typical Enid. What's not typical is her expression — part relief, part fury.

But before I can ask her what's going on, my bedroom door swings open, and my mother flies in.

"Enid, what—" She sees me and flings herself into my arms. "Oh, Alice, thank God. Thank God."

I wrap my arms around her and pat her back gingerly. She weeps against my chest.

"What's going on here?" I look to Enid for answers, but she folds her arms across her chest.

"What's going on? We've been worried sick. Where the hell were you?"

Shit. "I went out for a walk."

"You've been gone more than twelve hours."

Double shit. I don't answer. My mother pulls away from my chest.

"Enid came over last night. To bring you some cookies she made. I knocked on your door. You didn't answer, and I thought you might be asleep, but that you'd want to see Enid. After she'd gone to such trouble." My mother touches Enid's shoulder with affection.

"You weren't here," Enid interjects. "Your mother couldn't believe it. We looked all over for you. Tried calling you. I sent you a dozen text messages."

"My phone died," I remember. I pull it out of my pocket and hold it up, as if that'll absolve me.

"We almost called the police," Enid points out. Her arms are still folded. Clearly pissed, and I can't say I blame her.

"Poor Heath's been out driving around all night looking for you."

"Heath?" A red flush covers my neck. Enid's older brother had been a peripheral part of our lives throughout our friendship, but there had always been something about him that had made my stomach flip a little. I chalked it up to the fact that I had no brothers of my own, no male friends — how was I supposed to know how to act around a guy like that? I found his brooding intensity discomfiting.

"Oh, Enid, call him," my mother says. "Let him know she's back."

"Good idea." She whips out her own phone and turns away, speaking in a low voice.

"Where were you, Alice? My God." My mother wrings her hands in front of her chest; I realize suddenly how frail she's looking these days. Shorter than both Enid and me, with narrow shoulders which are still trembling.

"I'm sorry, Mom. I was feeling a bit better, so I decided to go into the city. To see a friend from work. Her boyfriend broke up with her and she's having a hard time and..."

"And you couldn't tell me? Really, Alice? You know how I worry."

Worry isn't even the word for it. "I know, Mom. I'm really sorry." And I am. I feel like absolute shit. I know that I'm twenty-five years old and most people my age are allowed to come and go as they please. But those people don't still live at home, with a mother whose blood pressure shoots up to dangerous levels every time the phone rings.

Enid disconnects the call with her brother. "He's heading

back to the house. I think I'm going to go home, too. Mrs. Brewster, are you going to be okay?"

"I am, dear, thank you. Really. You've been such a blessing. And please tell Heath thank you, too."

"I will."

Without another glance at me, Enid bounds down the stairs. I watch her go, feeling strangely bereft. And shitty. Mostly shitty.

"I suppose you'll want to spend the day sleeping," my mother sniffs.

"No, no," I lie. "I'm fine."

"Good. Because it's the last Saturday of the month."

I try not to groan. The last Saturday of the month is when we polish all the floors in the house, which means I'll be spending the day on my hands and knees. I cast one longing glance at my bed and plaster a smile on my face. "Let's do it."

Later, after we've rubbed and buffed every inch of hardwood in the house, my mother goes to lie down. Even though I'd give my left arm to do the same, I let her know that I'm heading out for a bit. She eyes me suspiciously, but I tell her I'll be home in no more than an hour.

Outside, the weather is beautiful, but the sun is a laser piercing my eyes. My stomach swims, but I force myself to put one foot in front of the other. I walk all the way to Alfonso's, the best bakery in Staten Island, and buy two half-dozen cannolis, plus one extra. I eat the extra cannoli before I even leave the shop and start the long walk home.

I expect to feel like death by the time I get back, but I don't. Maybe it's the sun or the fresh air or the life-giving properties of a good Italian pastry, but I feel somewhat human. I knock on Enid's door.

It's Heath that answers. My neck flushes again. "Hi."

"Hi." He folds his arms. His skin is pale, like Enid's, but where her features are delicate and elfin, his are more rugged, mysterious, his eyes dark. The kind of face you might see in a vintage whiskey ad.

"I'm sorry you had to spend last night driving around looking for me. I feel like a total piece of shit."

He doesn't answer, which I take to be an agreement of that assessment. I thrust out one of the pastry boxes.

"A peace offering," I say.

He grabs the box and turns, leaving the door open behind him. I take that as an invitation and step inside.

I've been inside Heath and Enid's house so many times that it's almost as familiar as my own, but I still experience a rush of warmth when I step into their kitchen. The room is a little dated, but nothing too extreme. No harvest gold appliances or anything. It's just... cozy. The fridge and stove are white, and they have a dishwasher — lucky — and Renata, their mom, has a rooster theme to her decor, with lots of plucky little red-capped birds winking at me from the walls and the countertops. One even peeks his head out of a neat stack of copper mixing bowls. It's a warm kitchen; friendly. The kind of place I used to come to get away from my own home. My own life.

Heath sets the pastries on the counter and turns on the coffeemaker.

"You don't need to—" I start, but he raises his eyebrows.

"You look like shit, Malice."

I take some comfort at the use of his old nickname for me. "Thanks a lot, Death." I slip onto one of the wooden chairs at their big, round kitchen table. "Is Enid home?"

"I'll get her."

By the time Enid and Heath return to the kitchen, the coffee is almost brewed and the smell is making me pulse with a sort of toxic desire. While Heath pours three cups, I push the pastry box toward Enid.

"I'm so sorry about last night," I say. "I'm an asshole." I feel bad enough for worrying my mother, but equally bad for lying to Enid and telling her I was sick. There's really no excuse for what I did, except that I feel the same way about Taylor as I do about the coffee that Heath is pouring. Like I need her. It's not a feeling I'm comfortable with, but I don't know how to fight it.

"Yeah," Enid says. "You are." But she takes the box and picks out a pastry, licking the sweet cream filling from one end.

Heath passes me a blue mug, and I slurp the coffee greedily. Caffeine courses through my veins like a magical elixir, restoring my energy levels and making me feel halfway human again. "This is great, thank you."

Heath utters a cranky sort of growl and buries his head in the fridge, looking for milk.

"So what was so important last night that you had to blow me off?" Enid asks as she nibbles the end of the cannoli.

I flush. "It's this other friend of mine. She was having a hard time. She begged me to come."

"You didn't think to tell her you had plans?"

I shrug. It had occurred to me, of course. For about five seconds, before I dismissed the idea. Nothing was going to stop me from seeing Taylor.

I take a second to think about how crazy that is. I only met Taylor a few days ago, and already she has me bailing on plans and sneaking out of the house like a rebellious teenager. That can't be healthy, can it?

"You look different," Enid says, squinting at me. "Are you okay?"

"Just tired." Not a lie.

"I don't just mean today."

Her scrutiny makes me squirm. I look to Heath to lighten the mood, but he's leaning against the counter, arms folded across his chest again.

I drain the rest of my coffee. "Thanks again for being with my mom last night. And sorry for being a shit."

I bolt from the house.

At home, my mother's up and watching TV. I give her the second box of pastries, along with another apology, and make us a quick dinner of pasta again before finally retiring to my bedroom. Even though it's barely seven o'clock, I can't wait to collapse onto my bed and sleep the rest of the night away.

But right as I'm about to drift off to a blessed dreamland, my phone buzzes. I almost don't pick it up, but one word in my mind makes me do it anyway: Taylor.

When I glance at the screen, I find that sure enough, it's her.

"Party tonight in East Williamsburg, want to go?"

I close my eyes and groan. I picture crawling into bed and sleeping for two days. I picture the disappointed way that Enid looked at me earlier.

But I already know that I'm not going to say no. I have an almost compulsive need to see her again. Somehow, being in her presence makes me feel as if my life is different. As if *I'm* different. A newer, better version of myself.

"Hell yes," I text back. **"Just tell me where."**

TEN

"COME ON, SAMMIE." The pretty woman held out her hand. "Don't you want to play in the sandbox with Alex?"

The little girl looked toward the sandbox where a boy just a bit bigger than her was loading handfuls of soft sand into a yellow plastic dump truck. It did look like fun.

She gazed up at the pretty lady, whose name was Julie. Julie nodded and gave her a little nudge forward. "There you go. Have fun."

Sammie walked slowly over to the sandbox. Alex didn't look up. He never said too much to her, but she didn't mind him. He wasn't rough like some boys she knew. There were four kids who lived in this house with Julie. There was her and Alex and two bigger kids who got to wear backpacks and go to school every day. She could go to school soon, they said. One more year. There was a man who lived in the house, too, and he slept in Julie's bedroom and he was called Rod, like a fishing rod. He was Sammie's favorite. He liked to sit on the floor and play blocks with her and sometimes he tickled her, but he always stopped as soon as she said so. He was nothing like the monster men who used to visit her mama.

She hadn't seen her mama in a long time. She wasn't sure how long. She missed her, sometimes, but she liked Julie and Rod and Alex and Misty and Carl. She never felt scared here. At night, she got to sleep in her own bed, and there was a little butterfly light that made it so that the room was never really dark. Also, Julie always left her a cup of water beside the bed so that she wouldn't have to get up in the night. She liked that. The house never had any strange noises or strange smells. There were no monsters.

She stepped over the edge of the sandbox and let her foot sink into the soft, powder-like sand. Alex barely looked up, but pushed a plastic tractor in her direction. She loaded up the shovel with sand and dumped it into Alex's truck. It poured out so smooth, like water. She laughed.

They played for a while. Julie sat on the step of the patio and watched them. The little girl had never known that some people had sandboxes right in their own backyards. Julie and Rod had a sandbox and a slide and two swings, too. She never wanted to leave. Maybe Mama could come here and live with all of them. Then things would be perfect.

After a few minutes, Rod came outside through the big patio door. The little girl was happy. She always felt happy when Fishing Rod was around.

But Rod wasn't smiling his usual smile, and his forehead looked wrinkled. He said something to Julie and then she didn't look happy, either.

"Come on, kids. Let's go in the house for a bit."

Alex stood without a word, but the little girl stayed

crouched in the sandbox. She was afraid to move. She didn't like when people didn't look happy.

"Come on, Sammie," Julie said. She smiled, but there was something wrong with it. The little girl didn't want to go to her.

Rod stepped down off the porch and held out his hand. "Come on, brave girl," he said.

She still didn't want to go, but she took his hand anyway, because she didn't want to disappoint him.

Inside the house, the little girl saw a woman she didn't know. The woman wore a skirt and the kind of scratchy nylons Mama used to wear sometimes. The little girl stood behind Fishing Rod.

"Hi Sammie," the woman said. "My name is Patrice. I'm from Social Services. I have good news for you."

The little girl didn't answer. She didn't want to leave Rod's side. It was like there was molten lava all around her, and if she went too far away from him, she'd fall in it and die.

The woman on the couch took no notice. She kept smiling and talking in a high-pitched voice. "You get to go home! Isn't that wonderful? You can go home to your mother now."

The little girl felt her stomach turn over, scrambling the grilled cheese she ate earlier. She looked up at Rod. Maybe Rod was coming, too. Maybe they would all go together, and Julie and Rod could help Mama get a sandbox and a butterfly light.

She reached for Rod's hand, but Rod didn't see. He had taken Julie's hand in his, and now he squeezed it tight.

Sammie let her own drop. There was no one to hold her hand here. No one could keep her from falling into the lava, after all.

ELEVEN

TWO HOURS LATER, as promised, I'm meeting Taylor in East Williamsburg. Once again, the address lands me in front of some anonymous brick warehouse that looks nothing like the scene of a hot party. But I guess that's what makes it so alluring. It's unexpected, mysterious.

There's no sign of Taylor yet, so I stand around outside for a while. The building is smack in the middle of a cluster of other buildings, so the main road is about a hundred feet away. There are a couple of streetlights struggling to illuminate the industrial complex, but the alley I'm stuck standing in grows darker and more ominous by the minute. The traffic is a distant hum, and this time there isn't even any music emanating from the building. I check my phone to make sure I'm at the right address — which I definitely am — and text Taylor to let her know I'm here.

"Be right there," she texts back.

I wait another few minutes. Footsteps echo from somewhere in the distance, getting closer. I expect to see

Taylor coming around the corner, but instead spot a man in a dark coat, a cap pulled low over his face, a black bag slung over one shoulder. He's heading straight toward me. There's nowhere to run, so I press my back against the wall, trying to appear as small and unobtrusive as possible.

But something about the short stride looks familiar, and as the figure gets closer, I recognize the jut of the chin, the pout of the lips.

"Taylor. You scared the crap out of me."

"You loser," she laughs. "But I know, not exactly my normal outfit."

She's wearing a bulky black jacket, bigger and even more unflattering than my own. Under that, she's wearing black leggings, black sneakers. Her blonde hair is tucked up inside a black wool cap. She looks more like a cat burglar than a party-goer.

"What's with the bag?"

She hoists it off her shoulder and gazes down at it for a second. When she looks at me, her expression is half playful, half embarrassed. "I might have lied to you. Just a little."

"About what?" My body is already tensing. "What's going on?"

"There's no party here."

"I kind of got that feeling." The warehouse beside us looms silent and dark. From the very back of my mind, a question: *just how well do you know this girl?* "So what are we doing here?"

"Come on," she says, instead of answering.

She heads further down the alley. I cast a glance around before turning and following her into the darkness. She's moving fast, and soon the streetlight is about twenty feet away from us, miring us in shadows. I look back at it longingly. Memories of the last time I followed Taylor down a dark alley — not to mention the poor guy we almost killed — float through my mind, but eventually I push them aside. In for a penny, in for a pound, right?

About halfway down the alley, Taylor stops so abruptly that I crash into her. She's standing in front of a dumpster, but she's looking at the wall above it. Or more specifically, the window.

"Hold this." She hands me the bag and vaults herself on top of the dumpster. She's way stronger and more agile than I expected for someone who's normally prancing around in stilettos. "Now hand it to me."

I reach up to give her the bag, from which she extracts a hammer.

"Ready?" She grins down at me.

"What are you—"

I don't even have time to finish the question. She ducks her head, covering it partially with the hood of her jacket, and she swings the hammer, hard, against the window. Glass shatters, falling down around her arms and into the garbage bin below.

"Taylor, what the fuck are you doing?" I look around nervously, expecting the cops to already be storming the alley. But it's as quiet — or as loud — as it was before Taylor broke the window.

She shrugs. "Easiest way in. Hope you can climb. Come on." She throws her backpack in through the window and holds her hand down to me.

Common sense tells me to walk away, but I'm tired of being common. I give my hand to Taylor and awkwardly hoist myself up onto the ledge of the dumpster with her. She wraps her jacket sleeve around her hand and uses it to clear glass away from the window ledge. I do the same, and soon the worst of the shards have been swept away.

"Give me a boost," she commands.

I loop my fingers together and let her put her sneaker-clad foot in it, using it to hoist her up to the window. She clambers inside. For a second, there's silence, and I'm worried she hurt herself falling over the side.

But then her grinning face appears in the window. "All clear. Come on."

She helps pull me through the window, and though I go over with even less grace than she did, eventually we're both inside.

My eyes struggle to adjust to the darkness. Beside me, Taylor fumbles in her bag. A burst of light illuminates the space as Taylor produces a camping lantern.

"You came prepared," I say.

"Always think ahead," she says, tapping her nose.

I examine our surroundings. There's nothing. It's just an empty warehouse. The ceilings are high, and pipes crisscross the space above us. The floor is poured concrete; the walls crumbling bricks that have seen better days. There's almost nothing in here, save for some construction materials — a stack of steel beams, enormous bags of insulation spilling cotton-candy pink. There's a smell of dust and a general staleness to the air.

"What the hell are we doing here?" I ask, thinking again

about how little I know Taylor. If she wanted to murder me, this would be the place to do it. It doesn't look like anyone's been here in months. I remember the hammer in her bag. "What is this place?"

"It used to be a bra factory, believe it or not. But not for a while. And soon it's going to be, I don't know, offices or something. Something boring like that."

"Okay. So why are we here, exactly?"

"Because." Taylor grabs her bag from where she'd tossed it earlier and produces a can of spray paint with a neon orange cap. She tosses it to me and takes out another one for herself, this one capped in an equally eye-watering green. "What matters isn't what this place was, or what it's going to be. What matters is who owns it."

"And who would that be?"

Taylor gives me a pointed look.

"Weston Chambers?" I blanch.

"The one and only."

"Taylor, what are you... we can't—"

"We can. You can." She shakes the can and uncaps it. She lets the paint loose against the wall. She takes her time spelling out the words RAPIST PIG in foot-high letters, all across the crumbling brick, while I watch, completely and utterly transfixed.

"Taylor, we're going to get caught. What if there are security cameras here?" But I keep staring at those words, the bold violence of them, the aggression of them.

"There aren't. I scouted it out earlier today. Just one at the front of the building, but since we didn't come in that way..."

I close my eyes. For a minute, I let myself imagine that I'm back home, away from this. Or even better, in Enid's basement with her, watching *Back To The Future* or some other eighties movie the way we were supposed to last night. Even Heath could be there, I wouldn't care. Just anything but this. This is too much. It's too...

"Here. Start with this."

I open my eyes and find Taylor thrusting a full bottle of whiskey at me. I grab it gratefully and take a long swig. The burn in my throat as it goes down unzips something in me.

I take another fortifying swig and hand the bottle back to Taylor. I uncap my can of spray paint and cross the room until I'm standing in front of a bare brick wall. Before I even realize what I'm doing, my finger is on the nozzle of the can and I'm pressing down, feeling the shake as the paint flows out.

WESTON

The letters are even bigger than Taylor's, at least three feet high.

CHAMBERS

My finger cramps on the nozzle.

IS

Taylor stands behind me, her arms folded, a satisfied look on her face.

A RAPIST.

"Yes, girl," Taylor shouts. "Yes!"

It takes me forever to write all the letters, but when I cross that last *T,* it's with a sense of elation that borders on mania.

"Beautiful," Taylor says, pretending to wipe away a tear. "Absolutely beautiful."

She passes me the whiskey again, and I take another healthy swig.

"Got any more paint?" I say as I pass the bottle back again.

"Hell yeah, I do." She grins and whips out another can, this one in an eye-popping pink. She must have cleaned out the fluorescents section of the Home Depot spray paint aisle.

I write my next message on the concrete floor, right beneath the first message.

AND HE HAS A SMALL DICK.

Taylor dances around me and paints an obscene picture of a tiny penis next to my words. We both cackle. We pass the whiskey back and forth, spraying more images across the floor and walls. Penises, pigs, choice words. The more I paint, the freer I feel. Though that might have something to do with the alcohol, too. I can't feel my fingers anymore, and the room spins around me, a blur of poured concrete, exposed brick, streaked neon.

Eventually, the whiskey's almost gone and there's only one more can of paint, this one in yellow. Taylor bestows it on me with great gusto, almost toppling over in the process and dissolving into hysterical laughter.

We're so lost in each other, in our shared madness, that we lose sight of where we are, what we're doing. I'm shaking up the last can of yellow paint when the voice comes.

"Police! Stop what you're doing."

TWELVE

"RUN!" Taylor yells, before taking off at a sprint toward the window.

But me? I freeze. I can't move my legs. I stand as still as the Statue of Liberty, spray paint held aloft, until one of the two officers grabs me roughly by the arm.

Taylor is gone. The other officer lunges at the window, but she must be out of sight already, because he curses softly as he leans out over the edge. Her backpack is on the floor, and he picks it up on his way back over. I pray she wasn't stupid enough to leave her wallet or phone in it. Knowing Taylor, though, she probably wasn't. *Always think ahead,* she said. The thought makes me smile a little.

"What's so funny?" the officer, who's still gripping my forearm as if it's the last sausage at a summer cookout, growls.

"Nothing," I mutter.

He leads me out of the building and toward the squad car, the second officer trailing behind us with Taylor's backpack.

An hour later, the reality of my situation is starting to sink in. The officer tells me his name is Officer Danticat, which makes me laugh — Dainty Cat, I think, picturing a prissy Siamese picking her way across a table strewn with teacups and lace doilies. Or maybe it's still the whiskey making me laugh. Officer Danticat throws around words like 'trespass' and 'vandalism.' That sobers me up a little. Those are actual *crimes*.

He keeps pressing me for Taylor's name, but I plead ignorance. I say I just met her, that she was already in the warehouse when I got there, that she must be a vagrant, a street person. I tell him the backpack is mine. He doesn't seem to believe me.

Eventually, Officer Danticat sighs. "I have a daughter your age, you know."

What does he want me to say? Congratulations? I stay silent.

"I saw what you were painting," he says. "Is there anything else you want to tell me?"

I continue my silence. I don't trust my voice, and not just because the room is still spinning.

He stares at me for a long while. "I'm going to let you go with a citation," he says eventually. "Do you know what that means? You're still going to have to appear in court. But I'm not going to process you."

"Thank me," I say. "That means a lot to you."

He frowns. "I am, however, going to put you in holding until you sober up. You're going to need to have someone come pick you up in the morning."

I try to thank him again, but he brushes me off and leads

me to a cell with two other women. One is asleep, lying on her back on a long bench, one hand flung over her eyes. The other, a brassy blonde, sits on the floor, back to the wall. The blonde casts a curious gaze at me when I enter, but soon goes back to staring blankly ahead. That's fine with me.

I sit as far away from either of them as I can, choosing a bench against the opposite wall. I close my eyes, but I'm too pent up to relax. I think about my mother a lot when I'm in there. I told her before I left that I'd be spending the night at a friend's — I didn't want a repeat of her previous freakout — but eventually I'm probably going to have to tell her what happened. There are going to be court dates and who knows what after that.

I should have never followed Taylor into that building. I know that now. But every time I remember painting those bold, angry words on the wall, something lifts inside me. A happiness, a freedom, that I haven't felt in ages. Maybe ever.

Whatever happens, maybe it was worth it.

Eventually, I fall asleep. I guess that'll happen after you've been awake for two straight nights. But after what seems like mere moments of slumber, Officer Danticat returns. The other two women are gone, and I'm alone in the cell. I have a crick in my neck, and the fingers of my right hand are numb from where I was resting them between my head and the concrete wall.

"How are you feeling?" the officer asks.

I shrug.

"About what I expected."

Am I imagining it, or is he smiling faintly?

"You have someone who can come pick you up?"

"I think so, yes."

"Good."

He lets me use the phone. I know I can't call my mother, so I call someone else. Someone I know I can always count on, even when I'm an asshole.

"Hello?" Her voice sounds sleepy, confused. I can see by the wall clock that it's six in the morning.

"Enid? It's Alice. I need a *huge* favor."

Two hours later, I'm strolling out of the 90th Precinct into the brightest sunshine I've ever seen. I could almost forget the entire thing had even happened, except for the citation folded up and shoved deep into my wallet, with its strict orders to appear in court four weeks from now. And, of course, except for the sullen figure walking beside me.

Not Enid, but Heath. And man, is he pissed.

"How could you be so stupid?" he asks as soon as we've pulled away from the station.

I shrug, though he can't see it since his eyes are glued to the road and the heavy Williamsburg traffic.

"Seriously, Alice. Trespassing? Vandalism? Graffiti? What the hell were you even doing?"

"You wouldn't understand."

"Try me."

But there's no way I can tell him the truth. The look Heath gave me when he first saw me at the precinct was one of contempt laced with a hint of confusion. But if I told him about the rape, that would all change. He'd look at me with pity. Like I was a broken little thing. Damaged. I'd rather he think I'm reckless and stupid than to think that.

"We were just having fun," I say instead. "We weren't hurting anyone."

He doesn't say anything for a few minutes. I watch the city recede behind us as we make our way across the Verrazzano and back onto Staten Island. Eventually, he sighs and says, "You've been different lately."

"Different how?" I scowl.

"I don't know. You were always quiet, but now you're... I don't know. Missing."

Missing. Without knowing it, he's almost described exactly how I feel. Ever since *the thing* — no, the rape; let's call it what it is — I've felt like an essential part of me is missing. Weston Chambers took something from me that day, and the hotel took something else when they wrote that check.

Or maybe I gave that part away.

"I'm fine," I insist.

"Why'd you really bail on Enid the other night?"

"I told you, I had to help another friend."

"The same friend you were with last night? The same one who got you arrested?"

I don't answer him, which is answer enough.

He sighs. "Look, just don't forget who's always been there for you, okay? You know Enid wants the best for you. We — we all do."

My throat tenses, and for a terrifying moment, I'm sure I'm going to start sobbing. Of course, I know that Enid only wants the best for me. She's the only one who's always been there for me, who knew all our family secrets and never treated me any differently for them. She's the only one who saw the bruises the first time my father hit me. I still remember the way her face had crumpled at the sight of them, the way she'd wanted to go straight to the school guidance counselor.

"No way," I'd said, adamant. Getting a counselor — or anyone else — involved was the last thing I needed. We were walking down the corridor, halfway between first-period English and second-period biology.

"He's a terrible person," Enid spit. "You can't let him keep doing this. How far is it going to go?"

"It's not going any further."

"What do you mean?"

I shrugged. I didn't know exactly; I was only repeating what my mother had said the night before, when she'd pressed a frozen bag of peas to my abdomen, where he'd punched me. 'Enough is enough,' she'd said. "I think we're probably going to move to Colorado."

"Colorado?" Enid stopped dead in her tracks, her biology textbook slipping from her arms.

I picked up the book and handed it back. "My aunt lives out there. She tells Mom all the time that we can go out there whenever we want, that we can live with her. It makes sense." I said this with confidence, as if I had any idea what made sense for a woman trapped in the cycle of domestic abuse.

"Wow," Enid said breathlessly. She hugged her textbook tighter as we reached the classroom. "When are you going?"

I shrugged. "Three weeks, probably." My father's job was something involving manufacturing parts distribution. I had no idea what that entailed — he didn't talk about work at home, except to bitch about it — but I knew he spent the last week of every month on the road. If we were going to leave, I knew we'd do it then. Disappear into the night and let him come home to an empty house. Then pray he didn't come after us.

"Wow," Enid breathed again. "Your mom is really brave."

I scoffed. God, I still remember that. I *scoffed*. Thankfully, I had no time to say anything else, because Mr. Ridgeway had already started his lecture on pollinators and he shushed us as soon as we walked in.

Enid and I never discussed the topic again. Two weeks later, my father turned up dead, and still she never brought it up. I always wondered if she'd been able to put the pieces together, come to the same conclusion as I had. But she's never said a word about it. She asks no questions, demands no answers. Everyone deserves a friend like that, and I'm lucky enough to have one.

I spend the rest of the drive home looking out the window, while Heath remains blissfully silent.

———

I expect to hear from Taylor that day, but nothing. Not a peep. I'm vaguely insulted — shouldn't she want to check up on me? The last time she saw me, I was being manhandled by a cop with a porn-style mustache. Surely that warrants a *hey, are you okay?* text.

I think about reaching out to her myself, but something holds me back. Instead, I message Enid, apologizing again for bailing on her the other day and thanking her for sending Heath to my rescue.

But there's no response from her, either. All day long, my phone doesn't buzz once.

The only good thing about it is that I'm finally able to catch up on my sleep. After two nights with Taylor, I'm more bone-deep tired than I've ever been in my life.

I sleep for a good eight hours — almost the whole day. I get up, eat some canned soup with Mom, and go back to bed, where I sleep for the rest of the night. By the time I get up the second time, I actually feel like a human being again.

Which works out well, because my mother sticks her head nervously into my room and says, "Don't you have to work today?"

Shit. Right. My 'job.' As far as Mom knows, I still work at The Grant, and since today is Monday, I'm supposed to be there in exactly an hour.

I throw off the blankets, jump in the shower, and head out of the house in a hurry — all for a long day of doing nothing.

I ride the ferry into the city as I usually do. My phone is still silent — nothing at all from Taylor. Or Enid. I could choose to feel sorry for myself, I guess, but standing on the outer deck of the ferry, with the wind in my hair and that very particularly boggy smell of the Narrows, I realize I can also choose not to. I can choose to do something.

I fire off a text to Taylor. A quick, **"That was crazy, hope you're okay."** I scan my phone for a list of hotels in the city where I could drop off my resume. I might not have a job at The Grant anymore, but that doesn't mean I have to sit around like a sloth for the rest of eternity.

I head over to the library first and use their computers to update and print my resume. It's a flimsy, sad little document. Other than two years at The Grant, my employment history comprises a couple of months as a correspondent for my high school yearbook and a few babysitting gigs. But everybody has to start somewhere. I can make a king-sized bed with hospital corners in two minutes flat; that has to count for something.

There are dozens — probably hundreds — of hotels in the city, so I start near the library and work my way out. It's easy enough to go to the check-in counters or the front desk concierge and drop off a resume. At one place, The Manhattan Villa, the front desk clerk tells me they're in desperate need of some new cleaning staff and offers to go get the manager.

This could be it. I follow the manager to the central seating area in the lobby, where he scans my resume while I try to look as polished and professional as possible. Not easy wearing jeans, combat boots, and an oversized leather jacket, but I do an okay job of it — until he looks up and asks why I left The Grant.

I freeze. I can't exactly tell him the truth, but I haven't worked out what to say instead. One condition of my departure from The Grant was that they'd agree to give me a good reference, but I still need a reason for leaving. I flounder for so long that the manager eventually gets up and walks away, leaving me sitting there on the terra cotta-colored lobby chaise like a vagrant. I bolt for the front doors, red-faced and fighting back angry tears.

After that, I lose some of my steam. I still pass out resumes, but my heart isn't in it. There are probably people out there who'd be good at bending the truth to suit their needs. Those people would probably say that they took some time off to focus on personal projects, or that they parted ways for a difference of opinion. But I'm not one of them. I can't bend the truth that way. What happened to me is what happened to me, and that's all there is to it.

And since the truth isn't exactly interview-friendly, I'm stuck with it.

I check my phone every once in a while, and each time I do, my stomach twists a little further. I still haven't heard back from Enid, and there's no response from Taylor, either. For the first time, I wonder if maybe something happened to her after the cops showed up. I'd been so focused on myself, seeing as how I was the one who got caught — but what if something happened to her when she was running away? What if she twisted her ankle and is still lying in that alley? What if she accidentally bolted right out into the street and got hit by a cab and is lying in a hospital somewhere? What if she's hurt, or worse?

I wait an hour and send her another text. Just a nudge. **"Let me know if you're ok... ok?"**

By the time I've finished passing out resumes, it's late enough that I can head back home on the ferry. I never even made it to El Diablo for a drink today. I can't remember the last time that happened.

———

That night, I finally hear from Enid. I'm expecting a bit of a lecture, but her text merely asks if I want to hang out and watch a movie on Saturday. I type out a resounding yes and fire it back. I don't even bother asking what movie; we could rewatch *Look Who's Talking* and both its cringe-inducing sequels — a project she'd taken on for a podcast episode she'd done on the worst movies of the eighties — and I wouldn't care.

I still don't get anything from Taylor. Not that night, or the next day, or the day after that. I think about messaging her again, or even stopping by her apartment, but I don't want to be *that* friend. The truth is, Taylor and I still barely know each other. We hung out for one weekend. That's it. She doesn't owe me any of her time, or even an update on her whereabouts. She doesn't owe me anything at all.

But on Thursday, when I wake up, I bite back a relieved smile when I see I have a new message from her.

"Sorry babe. That was cRaZy for sure!!! How are u? Are u free tmrw nite? Need your help!! :S"

Maybe I shouldn't reply for a bit, make her sweat a little the way that I did. But it's silly to play games like that. I'm a grown-up. Instead, I message her back right away.

"I'm fine. My first night in jail. :O And ya, I'm free. What's up?"

"Tell u later. xo."

I'm filled with a strange sense of foreboding. The messages are innocent enough, but so far, every time I've hung out with Taylor, it's led to trouble.

What will Friday have in store?

THIRTEEN

I SPEND another two days passing out resumes, expanding my search beyond hotels and hitting coffee shops, diners, bars. I have no relevant experience, but somewhere out there, someone's got to be desperate enough to hire me, right?

On Friday afternoon, a few hours before we're scheduled to hang out, I get a text from Taylor.

"Wear black 2nite ok babe? Nothing illegal I promise."

Despite her promise and her laughing emojis, this directive does nothing to quell my sense of foreboding about tonight.

However, since my standard uniform is black anyway, I have nothing to worry about in that regard. I'm already wearing black jeans and a black leather jacket. I've got a grey t-shirt on underneath, but I figure that will be fine. Instead of heading back to Staten Island, I call Mom and let her know that I'm staying downtown to have dinner with a few of the girls from work. She tries to sound happy for me, but the unmistakable anxiety creeps into her voice when she asks what time I'll be home. I promise that I'll be back by midnight, and this time, I pledge to myself to keep that promise. Taylor will understand. She'll have to.

When I get to the address she'd texted, she's already there. At least I won't have to spend any time lurking in alleys waiting for her this time. She stands in front of a small brick storefront. The black awning above reads 'The Black Spot.' Taylor isn't the only one there; a line of people snakes halfway down the block.

"What's this?" I ask, when we're in speaking distance.

"Oh, thank God. I just could *not* do this by myself."

"Do what?"

Instead of answering, she thrusts a folded piece of paper at me. No, not a piece of paper. A program. *The Haunting of Liliane Flowers* it says across the front.

"We're... seeing a play?"

"Not just any play. My roommate's play."

"Oh. That sounds... fun." And not at all what I was expecting from tonight.

"No. Definitely *not* fun. First, I've heard her rehearsing the monologues for the last two months. They're bad. Painfully bad. Second, my roommate isn't the only person I know in the play."

She cracks open the program, and runs her finger down the cast list, stopping at a name about halfway down. Dominic Carter.

"That's my ex," she says. "And I *so* didn't feel like seeing him tonight. But Sarah will kill me if I miss her show."

"I get it," I say. "I'm like your emotional support dog."

"No!" she exclaims, before realizing I'm joking. "Well, yeah. I guess a little. But I'll pay you back in drinks instead of dog biscuits and head scratches, okay?"

"I don't know," I joke. "I was kind of hoping for some head scratches."

Taylor reaches up and scratches me behind the ear. I lean my head into her hand, letting my eyes flutter closed for the briefest of seconds. Realizing how odd that is, I open them again and find Taylor staring at me. I jerk my head away and, just as abruptly, she pulls her hand back. I plaster a fake smile on my face, but a strange distance settles in between us.

Thankfully, at that moment, the line into The Black Spot starts to move. Taylor and I take our place behind a couple of hipsters vaping from cotton candy scented e-cigarettes and ranting about the inferiority of digital music. I can see why Taylor advised me to wear black — everyone here is in a uniform of skinny black jeans, black jackets, black boots, black tunics. I'm surprised I don't see any black berets, but I suppose that would count as trying too hard.

We eventually file into the building, which isn't so much a theater as a blank space that's been painted black. Hence the name, I guess. Wooden risers, also painted black, have been set up, and on them sit rows of beat-up metal folding chairs. Taylor and I shuffle into our seats and wait in silence. The disquiet between us lingers, and I try to come up with something clever to say, something that will make it all evaporate. Nothing comes to me.

The show starts about fifteen minutes later. There's no curtain, so the room floods with darkness as the house lights go down, then a spotlight illuminates the stage. Which again isn't so much a stage as a black floor about fifteen feet away from us. There's not much of a set, either, just a table and three chairs. In the background sits a steamer trunk, an old bicycle, a harp.

A raven-haired girl floats onto the stage wearing a gauzy white nightdress. Taylor elbows me. "That's her," she whispers.

I look at the program. Sarah Constantine. She's playing the titular Liliane Flowers.

"Have you ever seen a ghost?" Sarah-as-Liliane says to the audience, her voice powerful enough to project all the way to the cheap seats in the back. "Have you ever *been* a ghost?"

Oh good, we're breaking the fourth wall. I try not to roll my eyes, but Taylor squirms with laughter beside me. Sarah-as-Liliane lifts her arms. The thin white material of her oversized nightgown sleeves hangs down, making her look as if she has pale white wings.

"We're all ghosts," she says. "In one way or another, we're all ghosts in our own lives."

The play continues on like that. There's not much of a plot, but from what I can piece together, Liliane Flowers is a ghost who's haunting her former husband and his new lover. You're supposed to think that the husband, the subject of her vast rage, is the one who killed her. But in the end, it turns out to be the husband's new lover. Twist!

Taylor elbows me every time her ex comes on stage — he doesn't play the husband, but the husband's brother, Frank, who I think is supposed to have been in love with Liliane. In one scene, he and Liliane occupy the stage alone and have some sort of weird simulated ghost sex. I get why Taylor wasn't keen on this play. It can't be easy to see your ex-boyfriend humping your roommate, even if it *is* weird simulated ghost sex.

When the lights finally come back on — after a very, *very* long two hours — I'm surprised that a few audience members are wiping away tears. I presume they're tears of laughter, until I overhear one woman say earnestly, "Oh my God, I'm gutted!" without even a trace of irony.

"Powerful," her companion gushes.

Taylor and I take one look at each other and burst out laughing, earning us glares from everyone around us. We hurry back outside, where the sun has gone down and the evening has turned dark and cold.

"Did you want to wait around to see your roommate? Tell her congratulations or whatever?"

Taylor laughs some more. "I'll see her at home. If I try to talk to her now, I might start laughing, and that would be catastrophic. Come on — let's go get a drink. I need one after that."

"I know what you mean," I say. "I feel like a ghost in my own life."

Taylor snorts and starts walking, but I feel a pang of something uncomfortable. Just the other day, I'd talked to Heath about how I'm missing from my own life. There's not much difference between being missing and being a ghost. We're all alienated in some way, aren't we? We're all just trying to find somewhere to belong, to be whole.

Surprisingly *verklempt*, I follow Taylor down the street. A couple of blocks away, she stops in front of a pub-style bar called The Snooty Badger. "This okay?"

"Great."

We go inside and find a booth, order two pints of dark red beer.

"Your roommate was pretty good," I say, trying to be charitable. "I mean, regardless of the play. She's talented."

"Yeah, she's okay." Taylor swirls her drink. "I tried out for that play, too, but..." She shrugs.

"That's probably for the best. You don't want ghost sex on your resume," I try to assure her.

"Good point." She grins, but there's still a note of disappointment in her tone. "Anyway, thanks for coming with me. I don't think I could have sat through that by myself."

"No problem. This is my first real New York City play. Do you think this would be considered off-Broadway?"

Taylor snorts. "Yeah, right. That play was to Broadway what New Jersey is to New York — as in, not even the same state."

"Fair enough." We lapse into silence for a minute, drinking our beers, each of us thinking our own private thoughts. "So your ex... what's the story there?"

"Uhhh, what's the story? He was a douchebag. Isn't that always the story?"

"The handsome ones always are, it seems."

"Tell me about it."

"What particular flavor of douchebag was he?"

Instead of answering, Taylor slips into silence. She sips her beer.

"Sorry, I shouldn't have pried," I offer, sensing I've overstepped. "Exes are exes for a reason, right? That's good enough."

"No, no, you're fine. I was just trying to think about how to describe it." She splays her hands across the old wooden table. "He was very... belittling."

"Oh."

"I mean, I don't know if I'd call him abusive, exactly." She looks thoughtful, studying her beer. "But he liked to make me feel small. It was almost a compulsion with him. It didn't help that we were both in the acting field. If I had any kind of success at all, if I got a call back or booked a part, he'd imply that it was only because the director wanted to sleep with me. Or insinuate that I had already slept with him. He was like that with everything. If I cooked dinner, he'd point out the flaws — the chicken was overcooked, or I'd used baby carrots when I should have coined them myself. Stuff like that. Nothing was ever good enough for him."

"I'm sorry." I swallow. I've never told Taylor anything about my father, but what she's describing sounds so much like what I went through with him. What my mother went through. Of course, she suffered the physical abuse, too — the slaps, the punches, the kicks, the God-knows-what-else. But I wonder if the constant berating wasn't the worst part. There are only so many times you can be told you're worthless before you start to believe it.

She shrugs. "I'm just glad I was strong enough to see it.

Like I said, I'm not sure I'd call him abusive exactly, but it had the potential to go down that road. I was able to see him for what he was — a small man trying to make everyone seem smaller — but not every woman is able to do that. Some of them would have believed he was right. A lot of them, probably. It tears you down after a while. You start to believe the lies. You get smaller and smaller, until there isn't anything left of you at all."

I nod and nod and nod while she's talking. I see my mother — and myself, if I'm honest — in her words. My mother had let my father walk all over her. Not because she was weak, but because he'd broken her down. It wasn't until the first time that he hit me that she found the strength to make the ultimate sacrifice.

Taylor's face in the dim bar lighting looks thoughtful and sad. Something squirms in my stomach. I like her so much in that moment that it makes me physically uncomfortable. I've always thought of myself as straight, but for a hot second I consider the possibility that maybe these feelings for Taylor are crossing over into something romantic. I contemplate kissing her — leaning across the table and rubbing my thumb over her bottom lip, bringing my mouth down to cover hers. I test the thought like a loose tooth, prodding at it, judging the sensations it generates.

But there's nothing. No flash of lust. No flushing of my skin, no quickening of my heart, the feelings that usually come when I think about kissing someone I'm interested in.

Not that that happens very often. The last time I kissed someone was Chris Rossi, a guy I'd had a crush on in high school and had run into once at a convenience store a few years ago. He'd invited me to his house to 'watch a movie,' which turned out to be code for 'make out while some Japanese anime played in the background.' When I'd looked at Chris and thought about kissing him, I'd felt all the usual things. The racing heart, the flushing skin, the heat between my thighs.

Thinking about kissing Taylor does nothing for me. *To* me.

So the thing I feel for her isn't a crush exactly. But it's something. Something I've never felt before, something I have no words to describe. A girl crush, I guess you could call it, though the phrase hardly does it justice. I want to spend all my time with her. I want to absorb her somehow. I want to *be* her.

"Earth to Alice," she laughs. "Where'd you go?"

My skin flushes, though this time it has nothing to do with desire and everything to do with embarrassment. "Sorry. Just thinking about what you said. I'm really glad you got away from that guy. You're really strong."

"I've had to be," she mutters. She takes a sip of beer and sets the glass down with a thud. "You're strong, too, Alice. And that's why we should kill Weston Chambers."

"What?" I hiss. "We're not killing him. And keep your voice down."

"Come on, Alice. He deserves it. You know he does. Guys like that think they can just do this shit. That they can hurt us, make us feel small, take away our power. And we let them. We sit there and let them take it. What does that say about us?"

I have no answer for her. Maybe it says that we've had centuries of conditioning, and it's hard to fight history. Maybe it says that it's scarier to fight back than to sit back and take it. To smile pretty. Maybe it says that we don't want to stoop to their level.

My mother's face flashes in my mind. The determination that day she told me that my father had hit me for the last time, that she was finally ready to do something. The way she had stood at the front door, silent and stoic, when the police arrived at our house to tell us he was dead.

We don't all sit there and take it. Sometimes, some of us get pushed too far.

"Anyway," Taylor continues. "I know you're not allowed at The Grant, but I thought I could get a job there. Cleaning, just like you. Then I'll be able to find out when he's coming again. I can do it right before his room is supposed to be done. There'd be no reason for them to look at me. I have no relationship to him, zero motive to kill him. It'd be clean."

"You can't," I sputter. "You can't just... kill him." I lower my voice to a hiss again.

"I'm doing this for you, Alice." Her voice turns dark, low, almost hollow. "Some people deserve to be punished. Eventually, we all get what's coming to us."

"You're crazy," I whisper.

"Am I crazy? Or are you being a doormat?"

I look around the bar, then down at my beer, then finally at Taylor. I stand up.

"I'm sorry. I don't want to talk about this anymore. I'm going home."

"Alice, wait—"

I yank twenty bucks from my wallet and toss it on the table. "Sorry, Taylor. I have to go."

"Alice, I'm sorry. Please stay. We can talk about this. We don't have to..."

But I never find out what we don't have to do, because I'm already at the door and back out into the chilly night air.

FOURTEEN

A WEEK GOES BY. I don't contact Taylor, and she doesn't contact me. But not a day doesn't pass that I don't at least think about messaging her.

Maybe I'm overreacting. After all, there's no harm in daydreaming about killing someone. It's not like I haven't done it myself. Plenty of times, I've imagined holding a gun to Weston Chambers' head, forcing him to beg for mercy before coldly pulling the trigger and putting a bullet in his brain. Some nights, that fantasy is the only thing that finally lulls me to sleep.

So I get the impulse. But the reality is far more discomfiting than the fantasy. And every time I manage to convince myself that Taylor wasn't being serious, I remember the excited gleam in her eye at The Snooty Badger. The way she'd leaned across the table, her expression serious and determined. The conviction in her voice when she said, "Eventually, we all get what's coming to us."

Thankfully, I have plenty to keep me busy this week. To

my vast surprise, I get a call back from one of the places where I'd dropped off a resume last week. It's a small diner called Donna's, in midtown Manhattan. Not all that far from The Grant; in fact, I'd eaten there a couple of times before losing my job. The pay is crap, but it's something to keep me busy, and, let's be honest, I don't really need the money, not now that I'm a half-a-millionaire. What I need is something to get me out of the house every day, something to help me feel like I'm actually a contributing member of society again.

I go in for what I think is an interview, but Donna herself hands me an apron and a notepad and puts me to work.

Consider it a trial run, she tells me. Silver streaks her dark hair, which she wears pulled back into a massive bun at the back of her head. By the size of it, I guess her hair must be waist length, at least. Her hands are lined and look far older than her face. Years of washing dishes, maybe.

I don't do amazing at the waitressing gig, but I don't do horribly, either. I initially mess up a couple of orders before I realize how haphazardly the kitchen is pushing things out. Eventually, I figure out that if I go back there every half hour and reorganize the order slips, things come out in a more organized fashion. My efficiency must count for something, because Donna tells me to come back the next day, so I do.

When I'm not at Donna's, I'm helping Mom around the house or hanging out at Enid's. It's a way to ease my guilt after my shoddy treatment of her, but also, being around her seems deliciously normal after the time I've spent with Taylor. Enid and I burn through a dozen of her favorite classic movies, from *Tootsie* to *Terminator*. Even Heath, constantly crashing our evenings and throwing himself down on the couch between us, doesn't bother me.

But throughout it all, a secret part of me is always thinking of Taylor. I'm glued to my phone, sneaking peeks at it every chance I get. Always waiting for a text from Taylor, or fighting the urge to text her myself. It's a constant nagging itch, the thought of her out there. Every time I'm helping Mom clean out a closet or sort through a pile of old clothes, I wonder what Taylor's doing. Every time Enid and I are cackling over some retro comedy, I wonder what Taylor's doing. Every time Heath is needling me about my new career in waitressing — the Mistress of Meatloaf, he calls me — I'm thinking about what Taylor is doing.

On Friday, I almost expect to hear from her. We've spent the last two weekends together, and I wonder if she's thinking about that, too. But no message comes. I go to bed listless and more sad than I'd like to admit.

I take forever to fall asleep, so I'm still awake at three a.m. when my phone buzzes. I swipe for it, knocking it off the nightstand and fishing around for it on the floor. I don't realize I'm holding my breath until I let it out in a whoosh.

Taylor.

"I miss you," the message says. Just that.

I sit with the phone for a minute before texting back, **"Me too."**

There's no reply. I lay awake for hours, but no more messages come.

Eventually I fall into a fitful sleep, and when I wake up on Saturday morning — or more accurately, Saturday just past noon — the first thing I do is check my phone. There's another message from Taylor.

"I'm sorry we fought. Come over for dinner Sunday."

I only debate for a half second before I text back. **"Ok."**

———————

Sunday night, I arrive at Taylor's with a bottle of wine and a bouquet of tulips. I'm as nervous as if I were going over for a date. Outside her building, I panic and ditch the flowers in her apartment building's garbage bin then buzz into her apartment.

Taylor swings the door open before I can even knock.

"I brought wine," I say, thrusting it out to her.

"You're so sweet. Thanks."

She gives me a hug. I should have kept the flowers.

"Is your roommate home?"

"Nope. At the boyfriend's again."

"Is her play still going on?"

Taylor freezes for a second. Then she shakes her head. "Honestly, I have no idea. She's been at her boyfriend's all week. I can't remember how long the run was supposed to be."

"Have you had any auditions lately?" I don't know if that's a safe topic or not. Taylor rarely talks about her acting life.

But her face relaxes. "Only one this week. A beer

commercial. But they wanted someone younger, so I doubt I'll get a callback."

"Crazy. How old are you? Twenty-two? Twenty-three?"

She smiles. "Flattering. I'm twenty-five."

The same age as me. That surprises me, actually. Something about Taylor is so youthful and vibrant that I would have put money on her being younger than me. Then again, she probably hasn't lived through all the shit that I have. Her face is unmarred by the hardness of life.

Listen to me; I sound like an old crone.

"Come on. Let's have a drink. Should we open this wine?" She holds up the bottle I brought.

"Sure."

Taylor leads me into the kitchen, which is in complete disarray. Bags of groceries tumble over the counter; a leafy head of romaine lettuce protrudes from one, and tomatoes spill out around it. A baguette thrusts out of another. On the stove, two pots are simmering. Well, one is simmering. The other is boiling over.

"Sorry, I'm not much of a cook," Taylor says, rushing to the stove and removing the lid on the bubbling pot. "I'm trying to make pasta but..."

"I'm sure it'll be great. Want me to pour the wine?"

"That would be fabulous."

"Where are your wine glasses?"

Taylor stares up at the cupboards for a second before she points to the one closest to the fridge. "That one."

But in the cabinet, instead of wine glasses, I find a basic collection of baking goods — a jar of flour, one of sugar, a small tin of baking powder. A box of salt. "No wine glasses here."

"Sarah's always rearranging things. Try the next one over."

I open the next cabinet and find plates and bowls. In the third cabinet I find the wine glasses, along with an assortment of coffee cups and drinking glasses. One of the cups says Goldman Sachs. I laugh.

"Who worked at Goldman Sachs?" Not exactly what I expected from a couple of wannabe actresses.

Taylor keeps stirring the pasta, not looking at me. "That's Sarah's. Or her boyfriend's, technically. I think he worked there for a while, or one of his old roommates did. You know how these things get passed down."

Taylor sounds snippy, but I chalk it up to trying to focus on both the pasta and sauce at the same time.

I pour and hand her a generous glass of wine. "Here."

"You're a lifesaver." She drains a good portion of the wine and thrusts the glass out to me to top up, which I do.

"What can I do to help?" I ask. "Is this stuff going to be salad?" I grab the bag with the lettuce sprouting from it, and a yellow pepper spills out.

"Yes. If you could tear up the lettuce and chop a few veggies, that would be great. The baguette needs slicing, too."

"On it." I hunt around until I find a cutting board and a small paring knife.

"That knife sucks," Taylor says, turning. "There's a big one in the dishwasher. It's the only decent one we have."

"Thanks." I open the dishwasher and locate a large chef's knife. That'll do the trick. I set to work shredding lettuce and dicing the pepper. I mix up a dressing using some olive oil and balsamic vinegar that I find in the cupboard. It's obvious that neither Sarah nor Taylor cook very often; the cupboards only hold the barest of necessities.

Still, with just twenty minutes of work, we have a nice spread in front of us. Pasta, some kind of veggie-laden red sauce, salad, and baguette.

"There are cupcakes for dessert," Taylor announces when we sit down at the small two-person glass dining room table. "I couldn't resist stopping at Frosting Queen. Have you ever had their cupcakes?"

"No."

"They're amazing. I actually used to work there. I'm a Red Velvet kind of gal, but I didn't know what you'd like, so I got a variety. Okay, really, I just wanted an excuse to buy a dozen cupcakes."

"As if you need an excuse for that."

"Right?"

The awkwardness of the last time we saw each other has been forgotten. We eat our meal and laugh a lot while we talk about her roommate's play, her ex-boyfriend's bad hair, and my new job at Donna's. When she laughs so hard she snorts wine out her nose at my story of dropping a bowl of soup in a customer's lap, I get a strange pang of pride. Dropping that soup had been mortifying. I was so sure that Donna was going to fire me for it. She probably would have, too, if the customer hadn't been so chill about the whole thing. I'd kept my job by the skin of my teeth. But recounting the story to Taylor gives me enough distance to see the humor in it, and hearing her choke-laugh on her wine makes it more than a funny story. It becomes a gold coin I've paid to pass over to somewhere I didn't even know I wanted to be. A toll I didn't know I needed to pay.

By the time Taylor produces the box of cupcakes, I'm so full that I could burst, but I can't resist their sugary smell or the delicate frostings. I choose a yellow one from the top left corner.

"Lemon Meringue Zinger. Interesting choice," Taylor muses, taking her aforementioned Red Velvet. "Sour, bright, classic. Sounds like someone I know."

I flush. That might actually be the nicest thing anyone's ever said to me. "So what does Red Velvet say about you?"

She considers the cake in front of her. "I think it says I'm sweet, traditional, and just a bit extra."

"That sounds about right."

We finish our cupcakes; they really *are* extraordinary. When we're done, I start taking our dishes into the kitchen, but Taylor swats at me.

"Leave them. You're my guest."

"Are you sure? I don't mind helping."

"You've already done enough. Have some more wine." Taylor tops up my glass, which has already been drained and filled way too many times tonight. The room spins, my vision blurs. Still, I don't tell her no, and I take another sip from my now-full glass.

"So..." Taylor says once she's recapped the bottle. "I have to tell you something, but I don't know if I should."

"What do you mean? Of course, you should."

"You might get mad at me."

"Why would I get mad?"

"Because you might not like what I did. Even though I promise you it's for the best. I'm doing this to help you."

Suddenly, I know exactly what she's referring to. This is about Weston Chambers again. I don't know why she won't let this go, but she hasn't. "Taylor, no."

"I got a job at The Grant."

"No. Just... no. Taylor—"

"Hear me out."

"I'm not hearing you out. You're talking about *murder*." I hiss the word out low, as if even in Taylor's apartment, someone might overhear us.

"I'm talking about doing the world a favor. Weston Chambers' behavior is an open secret. Everyone knows who he is and what he does. But no one stops him. He just gets away with it, over and over. And he's going to keep getting away with it. Is that what you want? Is that what you want on your conscience?"

"It's not on my conscience," I spit. "It's on his."

"Please." Taylor laughs, but it's mirthless. "You think a man like that even *has* a conscience? Something happens to people when they're too rich, too privileged. Do you know what a conscience is? It's empathy for other people. It's looking at your own behavior and seeing the way it harms others. And if nothing bad has ever happened to you yourself, you can't imagine it happening to anyone else. If you've never known pain, you can't imagine anyone else's."

I stand up. I can't listen to this anymore. Because the truth is, what Taylor is saying makes sense. I know I'm not the first woman to get caught in Weston Chambers' web, and I hate to admit that I know I won't be the last. Of course, there's a part of me that wants him to die. That wants to make him pay for what he did to me, and to prevent him from doing it to anyone else. But I can't go down that road. I can't. I won't.

And I won't let her go there, either.

"I'm sorry, Taylor. I don't want this. I don't want you to kill him."

"I'm doing this for you, Alice."

"Then... then I forbid you."

Taylor cackles. "You *forbid* me?"

"Yeah. I do. You say you're doing this for me. Well, I'm telling you I don't want it. I don't want you to do it. I won't let you jeopardize your life like this."

"The wheels are already in motion, Alice, my dear." She leans back, folding her arms. "Weston Chambers is going to be in town on Friday."

FIFTEEN

I BLANCH. Friday. That's less than a week away. "You can't."

"I'm going to."

"You're crazy."

"Try and stop me." Taylor's eyes gleam. She looks so confident, so self-assured. So... terrifying.

"I think I should go," I whisper. I don't know what else to say. My wine buzz has evaporated, replaced by the buzz of anxiety.

"If you have to."

I expect her to put up more of an argument, but she says nothing else as I shrug on my coat and stuff my feet into my combat boots. She still says nothing as I stand at the front door of her apartment, my hand on the knob. She doesn't even look in my direction. She plucks another cupcake from the box, this one dark chocolate, and runs her finger through the bright pink frosting. She licks the frosting away, sucking at her finger until it's clean again.

I leave the apartment without saying a word.

I don't sleep a wink that night, even though I've had enough wine to knock me on my ass. I lay awake all night, staring at the ceiling of my bedroom, illuminated by a sliver of moonlight that creeps in from the space between the blind and the window frame. It paints the room in an ethereal silver light.

I try to tell myself that Taylor wasn't serious, that she won't actually go through with it, but every time I remember the steely glint in her eyes, my stomach rolls. I know she's an actress, but she sure felt serious to me.

I'll call her tomorrow, I decide. I'll talk to her rationally and logically, when we're both sober. I'll explain to her that as much as I hate Weston, I don't want her to kill him. I'll tell her I care too much about her to let her put her life in danger like that. To sell her soul for me. Maybe I'll even tell her about my mother, about what her decision has cost her. About what it took from her, to have my father's blood on her hands.

But even with that plan in mind, it takes me until past dawn to fall asleep.

The next day, I text Taylor. I tell her I'm sorry about how things ended last night and ask her if we can talk. The request is so reasonable that I expect an immediate reply, maybe even a mutual apology. But my phone stays silent. I wait all afternoon, my ass parked on a stool at the bar at El Diablo's, but not a peep from Taylor. I wonder if she's at The Grant already. If she's working, she likely won't have her phone on her. They didn't like us carrying them when we were on duty. Relief sags through me at that thought. Of course. She's working. She'll reply to my text when her shift is over.

But at four o'clock, when the day shift ends, no reply comes from Taylor. Give her time, I tell myself. Maybe her phone died while she was working, maybe she wanted to hurry home to shower. But the rest of Monday sails by with no response.

Monday night I send her another message. Just a nudge. Just a **"Hey, are we cool?"** Really casual, no pressure. All she has to type back is a simple 'we're cool.' Two words. Even a single 'y' would do the trick.

But there's nothing.

On Tuesday, I'm really starting to worry. I still haven't heard from her, and Friday is fast approaching. I try to tell myself that she won't go through with it, but the honest to God truth is I have no idea if she will or not. It feels completely crazy to say, but I actually think she might. It seems inhuman and insane, but something about Taylor as a whole has always seemed slightly inhuman.

But insane? I don't know. I really don't know her that well, and that thought alone scares me more than anything.

So on Tuesday, I give up texting and actually try calling her. The phone rings and rings before it finally goes to voicemail. I expect her voice, but it's a computerized recording reciting the number I've reached. I leave a quick message, not saying anything incriminating, of course. Just a quick, *hey, I'm worried about you, give me a call.* I hope the 'please don't murder anyone' is implied.

That night I go to Enid's and join her down in the basement. I've seen more of her over the last two weeks than I have in the last two years combined. But this time I'm unable to lose myself in her pick of *Evil Dead.* When I check my phone for the four hundredth time, Enid rolls her eyes.

"Alice, if you have somewhere better to be, just go."

I stuff the phone back into my pocket. "Sorry. I was hoping to hear from someone. I'm worried about a friend, and she hasn't checked in. That's all."

"Oh. I'm sorry. Can I do anything?" Enid's pale face looks concerned.

I have to look away. "It's fine. I'll try to stop being so distracted."

"Are you sure? Do you need to go?"

"No, no. Let's just keep watching the movie. Is Heath coming over tonight?" Despite the fact that Heath ostensibly shares an apartment with a couple of roommates, he's almost always here. At least when I come over.

Enid wrinkles her nose. "No. I think he's on a date or something."

"A date? Really?" I try to sound incredulous, but my voice goes a little too high pitched.

"Can you believe someone would actually want to date my brother? Gross."

"Yeah, gross. Haha."

"Chips?" Enid thrusts the bag at me and I take a handful, but they taste dry and flavorless against my tongue.

By Wednesday, I still haven't heard from Taylor. I'm really panicking now. I just want to hear her say that she won't go through with it. If she doesn't want to be friends with me anymore, that's fine. I'll deal with it. I just need to know she isn't going to do anything stupid.

For the first time, I consider going to the police. They'd be able to notify Weston that he was in danger, suggest he stay somewhere other than The Grant while he's in town. But how do I do that without getting Taylor into trouble? If I went to the police, they'd want to know how I knew all this. Maybe they'd even think *I* was the crazy one. And that's if they even believed me. I can't see how it works without blowing back on at least one of us.

I could tell them she's having a mental breakdown, maybe. Have her involuntarily committed. Just briefly, just a forty-eight-hour psych hold or something. Just long enough for me to get to her, to talk some sense into her.

But I know I can't do that to her, either. First of all, I wouldn't be able to do it without explaining exactly why she's a danger to herself or others. And second, I just couldn't do it. My mother has spent her entire life living in fear of the psych hold. It was one of my father's recurring threats — that if she ever tried to report him for his abuse, he'd use her anxiety and depression as a means to get her locked up. Say she'd devolved into paranoia, psychosis. That she was threatening suicide. The thought of being locked up would send her into a full panic attack. I can't do that to Taylor. It would feel like a betrayal.

But I have to reach her somehow.

It's too bad I can't get to her right now, I think as I sit at the bar of El Diablo, drinking a gin and tonic, the Wednesday happy hour special. I'd finished my shift at Donna's at two, but Taylor's probably at The Grant, changing bedsheets and folding towels and — I shudder — fluffing curtains.

So why couldn't I talk to her now? Maybe it's the gin talking, but suddenly going straight to The Grant myself seems like the best idea I've ever had. Screw the order that says I'm not supposed to set foot in there again. This is more important than some bullshit legal agreement that I should never have signed.

I drop some cash on the bar and stumble out of my seat. I'm more drunk than I thought I was. Damn those half-priced drinks. I stagger to the door and step outside, blinking against the bright sunlight. I summon an Uber and a few minutes later, we're pulling up in front of The Grant.

SIXTEEN

MY STOMACH DIPS at the sight of the familiar ornate facade of The Grant Hotel. The brass and the glass and twin eagle heads on either side of the grand front doors. The last time I set foot in this building was the day of *the thing*.

I try to take a couple of steps forward, but my feet refuse to move. I stand outside, on the sidewalk in front of the building, but as far from the doors as I can physically get. I rarely used this entrance — the cleaning staff largely entered and exited via a back door — but since I no longer have a pass, I'll have to go in through the front doors like a regular guest.

Of course, that increases the odds of someone seeing me. I picture one of the burly security guards grabbing me by the arm and physically dragging me from the building. They're always lurking around the lobby, never venturing far from the front entrance, trying to blend in with their crisp suits, but unmissable thanks to their builds, their postures, their gazes, and just about everything else.

I stand out there for a few long minutes, but that's

probably even more suspicious. I decide to walk half a block up to where I know there's a huge souvenir kiosk, the kind that flogs t-shirts and mugs and knee-high soccer socks that all loudly proclaim *I <3 NY*. But most importantly, they also sell hats.

I pick out a black baseball cap. This one doesn't say anything, but has the outline of the state of New York embroidered on it, which is at least a little more subtle. I also grab a pair of dark sunglasses while I'm there.

With my new disguise, I walk back up to The Grant. This time I don't hesitate. I know if I do, I'll never make it inside. I walk straight up to the door, pausing for only a fraction of a second while they automatically slide open. Then I'm striding through the lobby, acting as if I belong there, acting as if the fresh-lily-and-cleaning-polish smell of the place doesn't make me sick to my stomach.

I go straight through the lobby and turn left down the maze-like hallways I know will eventually take me to the housekeeping break room. At any given time, there are usually at least a couple of people hanging out in there — which the hotel seems to think is enough to keep it secure. So there's no lock on the door, and no pass card required to get in, even though all of us have our lockers in there to store our valuables while we're working. Sure, the lockers have combination locks on them, but that's not nearly enough to stop an enterprising thief. That's how my wallet got stolen last time. Someone just strolled in and cut a few of the locks.

But as I push open the door unnoticed, I'm grateful for the lax security.

The break room is empty. All I find inside are the usual

tables and chairs, the familiar gurgling water cooler, the same tangy smell coming from the microwave. Considering this room is used exclusively by the housekeeping staff, it isn't kept particularly tidy. No one ever wants to be the one to clean the microwave, and it looks as disgusting as ever.

I let the door of the break room swing closed behind me. I pace nervously in the empty room, waiting for someone to show up. I don't really have a plan, other than to hope Taylor magically appears, or that I'll run into someone I know and can ask them to go track her down for me. Now that I'm here, the plan doesn't seem all that well formed. I don't know nearly everyone on staff. I'd recognize most of them by sight, maybe enough to nod hello, but I don't know their names and there are only a handful I'd feel comfortable asking to get a message to Taylor for me.

While I pace, I go over the room meticulously. I used to come in here at least twice a day, but the details of it are so bland that they've blurred together in my mind. Nothing is familiar, except in a banal sort of way: the blue walls, the linoleum floor, the fluorescent lights.

Over the microwave is a bulletin board with the current week's schedule pinned to it. I scan the list to see if I can figure out when Taylor is working.

Her name isn't anywhere on the schedule.

I look it over three times to be sure, but there's no Taylor. I don't even recognize half the names on here. There's a high turnover in this business, and I like to think The Grant is worse than average, but maybe I'm projecting.

I consider why Taylor wouldn't be on the schedule. Did she quit already? Maybe our talk had gotten through to her and she'd given up on this ridiculous idea of getting revenge on my attacker.

But it's also just as possible that the schedule is old. Maybe Zsuzsanna, our supervisor, didn't bother typing up a new schedule for this week. Taylor could be replacing someone on this list — Zsu could have just told her she was responsible for any shifts that had that person's name on it, without bothering to retype the whole thing.

There's no way to know for sure, and I have to get confirmation before I can relax.

Behind me, the door to the break room swings open.

"You aren't supposed to be in here," a thickly accented voice accosts me.

I breathe a sigh of relief. Short of running into Taylor herself, this is the next best thing. I turn. "Minnie!"

"Yes, miss?"

I realize she doesn't recognize me, so I pull off the hat and the glasses. Her lined face breaks into a smile.

"Alice, honey! What are you doing here?" She wraps me in a hug, and I breathe in the warm sugary scent of her. Minnie has worked here longer than anyone. She's only in her late thirties — maybe? — but she was a den mother to all of us. She's warm, unflappable, and kinder than anyone I've ever met in my life.

"I didn't know if I'd ever see you again," Minnie says. "You left so fast that day."

"Yeah. Some shit went down," I say, not wanting to get into it, but Minnie nods sagely.

"Terrible business. I'm so sorry. That bastard. They're all bastards," she spits.

"No disagreement here."

"No, I don't expect there would be. How are you doing, honey? Are you okay?"

"I'm okay." I shrug. I guess it's not totally a lie. I *am* okay. Okay enough, anyway. At least assuming I can find Taylor and ward off any impending catastrophe. "I'm actually trying to get in touch with a friend of mine. I haven't heard from her in a few days, and I'm getting worried."

"How can I help?"

"She was supposed to start working here this week. I was wondering if you'd seen her around. Her name's Taylor."

"Last name?"

I blank. I realize I have no freaking clue what Taylor's last name is. I shrug helplessly.

"Well, the only Taylor we've got here is Taylor Johansen, but she was working here when you started. That's not who you mean, is it?"

"No, no." I remember that Taylor. Swedish. Mean. "She's about my height, blonde, pretty." I remember the photo I snapped the other day at Karnival and pull it out. "This is her."

Minnie takes the phone and peers at it. I know the photo isn't the best — Taylor is in profile and her eyes are closed and the colored lights from the bar cast kaleidoscope shadows across her face, but it's the only one I have.

"Sorry, honey, I really couldn't say. She looks familiar, but..." Minnie stares at the phone a few seconds longer and shrugs. "I don't know. All you young girls blend together after a while. She could be anyone."

She *isn't* just anyone, though. That's what I want to say,

anyway, but of course I don't. "Thanks, Minnie. Can you call me if you see her? Or if anyone named Taylor shows up on the schedule?"

"Of course."

I leave my phone number with Minnie. Neither of us bother suggesting getting together for coffee or anything like that, because we both know it's not going to happen.

I pull my cap and glasses back on, bid Minnie goodbye, and head back down the maze to the hotel's main lobby. As I near the front doors, a voice rings out behind me.

"Hey! Hey you!"

I look back over my shoulder. Shit. It's Eldon, the prissy front desk clerk. I pick up my pace, but he follows me. "Hey! You're not supposed to be here, you know. You're not supposed to be here."

One of the security guards takes note and heads for me. They're both coming at me now, Eldon and a burly man with a huge shaved head and a small trimmed mustache.

I bolt for the door.

SEVENTEEN

THE AUTOMATIC DOORS of The Grant slide open, and I burst out onto the street. A school of Japanese tourists swims by on the right, and I try to disappear with them, letting them carry me down the block. After a minute, I risk a glance behind me. Eldon and the security guard have followed me outside. Neither of them leave the portico of The Grant, though; they just stand there, heads bent together, conferring on something.

I try to get my breathing under control, which is easier once I turn the corner and the hotel is no longer in view. That was stupid, showing up at The Grant like that. I try to reassure myself that there's nothing Eldon can do, or even anything he *will* do. Sure, he might have called the cops or let Security hassle me if I'd refused to leave, but he's not going to put up a fuss now that I'm gone. I might end up as a tiny notation in the day's security log, but that's about it.

After I've gone another couple of blocks, I throw the hat and the glasses into a garbage can. I haven't checked my phone in over an hour, so I whip it out. I'm somehow sure that I'll finally have a message from Taylor, but the screen is as blank as it ever was.

I debate sending her a message, letting her know I was at The Grant, but if she's still planning on going through with this, I don't want to spook her. The last thing I want is for her to panic and do something stupid.

The clock on my phone says four o'clock. Almost time to head home. Or should I go to El Diablo for one more drink? There's always a chance Taylor might stop in again. Wishful thinking, maybe, but that's where I first met her and the bar's not that far from here.

I round the corner toward the bar — hey, the happy hour prices should still be on, and what's one more drink and a little wishful thinking? — when my phone rings.

I almost drop it on the ground fumbling for it, and when I pull up the screen, I let out a whoop of relief. Taylor.

"Hi!" I exclaim, leaning against the stone exterior of a small sushi restaurant. "You're a hard woman to get ahold of, you know that?"

She laughs. Her voice on the other end of the phone is tinny and distant. "You're funny. I got all your messages, I'm sorry. I should have got back to you before this. I've just been so busy — yesterday night I had a date, and this morning I went to this open call for a cereal commercial. It was kind of a bust, but I got a callback for something else I'd auditioned for a couple of weeks ago. I didn't even have time to go home and change."

"That's great. What was the callback for?"

She laughs again. "This super cheesy workplace sexual

harassment video. I'm supposed to play the meek administrative assistant whose lecherous boss won't stop staring down her blouse. I don't think I'm going to get the part, though; I kept slapping the guy."

I laugh. "Taylor, you didn't."

"I couldn't help it! He was just so blatantly pervy. Clearly not even acting. So it was an instinctive reaction on my part. Every time he leered, I slapped. We ran through my part about six times, and the guy had a solid handprint on his face by the time we were done. They told me I could go."

By this time we've both dissolved into giggles. All my earlier paranoia seems like exactly that — paranoia. She asks me how Donna's is going, and I tell her about the customer who referred to grilled cheese as 'curled cheese' and the old man who only ever orders Ovaltine.

"Ovaltine," she sputters. "I didn't think you could even buy that stuff anymore. I think one of my... grandmas used to drink it."

"I'm pretty sure Donna keeps it on hand just for him," I say, ignoring the hesitation in her voice. "There's a huge crate of it in the kitchen."

"I'll remember that if there's ever an apocalypse."

"Right? It's literally a form of gruel. Definitely apocalypse food."

It feels good to talk to her this way again. Like we're normal friends and not co-conspirators. But I have to know for sure that she's not going to do anything stupid. Taking a deep breath, I start, "Hey, Taylor?"

"Yes, Alice, dear?"

"You know what we were talking about the other day?"

"What's that?"

"You know. About Weston."

There's silence on the other end of the phone. *Come on, Taylor. Don't make me say it.*

But she's going to make me say it.

"You know." I keep my voice low as a group of over-excited teenagers clutching oversized iced coffees scurries by. "How you were talking about killing him."

There's another beat of silence on the other end of the line. My stomach drops to somewhere around my knees. A sputter of laughter comes from the other end of the line.

"God, you're so gullible." She's laughing so hard she can barely breathe. "I can't believe you fell for all that. Oh my God — can you imagine? Me, kill someone?"

At last, the remaining tension leaves my shoulders. "I know, I know. But you were very believable. Maybe it's your acting skills."

"Well, thank you. I'll take that as a compliment."

"You should." I move away from the sushi restaurant and start walking again. "So you never got a job at The Grant?"

"No. Please. As if I have time for another job."

Phew. "You know, I actually went there today to look for you."

"You did?" She barks another laugh. "I'm sorry, I'm not laughing at you. I'm just..."

"No, it's okay. You can laugh. I was seriously freaked out." Only now, the feeling is already such a distant memory that I can barely even remember why I was so worried. As if Taylor would ever do something so extreme.

I round the corner and come upon the bar. "Hey, I'm in

front of El Diablo right now. Any chance you're in the area and feel like a drink? My alcoholism could use some company."

"Sorry, babe. I'm all the way across town. I've got a shift at the coffee shop today."

Right. I forgot Taylor mentioned she worked at a coffee shop. "No wonder you're so busy. How many jobs do you have, exactly?"

"It's only three days a week. Enough to buy, you know, like groceries and whatever."

"Cupcakes," I add.

"Exactly. The important stuff."

"Cool. How long are you going to be at the coffee shop? I could come by and say hi." I know I'm bordering on clingy, but there's a part of me that really wants to see her. Just to officially put my mind at ease.

"Till eight, but really, there's no point. It's packed with students this time of day. You'll never find a table. And I'd have no time to talk."

"Okay, sure."

There's a beat of silence, and Taylor says, "Let's hang out Friday, though, okay?"

"Sure, yeah. That sounds great."

"Cool. I'll text you later."

We say our goodbyes, and by the time I've disconnected the call, the weight of the world has been lifted from my shoulders.

Still, by the time Friday arrives, some of the tension has returned. I know Taylor said she had no plans of going through with anything, but just the very possibility of it nags at me. Or maybe it's knowing that Weston is here in the city again. Knowing that a few miles away, he's checking into The Grant, settling into his usual suite.

Knowing that I could confront him myself if I wanted.

Not that I want to, but...

Have you ever walked up to the edge of the cliff and thought about jumping? Even if you didn't want to, even if you had no intention of ever harming yourself? There's something about standing on the precipice that holds a certain power.

I know that I'll never confront Weston Chambers about what he did to me. In fact, if I ever came within twenty feet of him, I'd probably slink away and go throw up somewhere. But knowing he's here in the city sets my nerve endings aflame.

I haven't heard from Taylor since Wednesday, so before I leave for work, I send her another text asking if she still wants to get together today. Her texting responsiveness is hit or miss, so I'm not expecting a reply right away, and I'm certainly not expecting my phone to ring almost as soon as my missive goes through.

"Hey babe, great timing," Taylor gushes. "I was just about to message you, but I figured it was easier to call instead."

"Great." It's hard to match Taylor's enthusiasm on the best of days, but today she sounds positively manic. "Do you still want to hang out tonight? I thought maybe we could see a movie or—"

"I have an even better idea — picnic in the park!"

"Picnic. Okay, yeah, sure." I can't remember the last time I went on a picnic. Maybe never?

"You don't like it?" I can hear her pouting even over the phone. "I thought it would be fun. We could meet in Central Park. One last hurrah before the weather's officially too cold. I'll bring some stuff from Whole Foods. Their mac and cheese is amazing. Oh, and maybe some bubbly. Doesn't that sound fun?"

It does, actually, sound fun. Or maybe it's that Taylor's enthusiasm — not just for picnics, but for life in general — is infectious. "It sounds great, Taylor."

"Yay! I was thinking maybe around two thirty?"

"I work until two. How's three?"

"Perfection." She gives me directions to a specific meeting place in the park, and I promise to meet her there.

EIGHTEEN

SAM EYED them suspiciously across the dining room table. It wasn't that there was anything particularly wrong with this family — the Hartmans, they were called — it's just that she eyed all families suspiciously these days.

The wife, who was called Martina, said grace. Sam found her wholly unappealing. She had a pinched, unhappy face, and was clearly another one of those Jesus kinds, the ones who can always pull up a piece of scripture that suits them while conveniently ignoring the rest. She squeezed Sam's hand too tight as she said amen, her nails almost puncturing the skin.

The husband, though, he seemed all right. Sam still hadn't decided for sure. He was called Peter. He had a round, jocular face, and an equally round belly. He smiled a lot. Normally, Sam didn't like people who smiled a lot — it was one of those suspicious traits she was always on the lookout for — but it suited Peter somehow. He squeezed her other hand as she echoed Martina's amen, and he winked at her as if they were co-conspirators in something. She liked that, that they had their own secrets already.

She'd been with this family for a couple of weeks. There were no other children in the house, which was unusual, but actually had the potential to be a net positive. She didn't have to share a room, and there was no one to fight over dessert with. And Martina made her share of delectable desserts, Sam had to admit. The Jesus kinds were always excellent bakers.

In the end, she supposed it didn't matter how much she did or didn't like them. She'd only be here a few months, and then Evangeline would get clean again and Sam would have to go back to living in that hovel. Her opinion in the matter meant nothing. The consensus was that a child was always better off with her parents. Sam thought that was only an excuse, though, and now that she was twelve, she was thoroughly familiar with the ins and outs of the system. There were only so many foster homes, and if a parent was at all capable of taking their child back, well, they were just happy to have one less kid on the books.

After dinner, she helped Martina clear the table and load the dishwasher. Above the sink hung a wooden plaque. It had clearly been handmade, because the lettering wasn't completely uniform, as if someone had painted it in the throes of religious fervor.

"The Lord sees everything you do. Wherever you go, he is watching. -Proverbs 5:21."

She felt the words staring at her the entire time.

She spent the evening doing her homework in the dining room, where the plaque was still visible through the doorway. When she was done, Peter let her into the den to watch television with him. He was watching a show called The Sopranos. Sam wasn't all that interested in it, but it was a nice distraction. The den was quiet and dark. Martina sat in the corner near the only lamp, working on an afghan blanket in blaring yellows and greens. Sam sat on the couch with Peter. For a second, she let herself pretend she was their real daughter, but she stopped when the squirming feeling in her stomach got too strong. She had a mother, and that mother was Evangeline. That was her lot in life.

At nine, she went to bed. Martina watched while she said her prayers — which was really just Sam kneeling in front of the bed and counting to a hundred a couple of times in her head — and then left her in the dark bedroom. Sam listened to the creaks and groans of the house as Martina and Peter got ready for bed and disappeared into their own bedroom.

This house might be all right, she thought, as she drifted off to sleep. At least for a while.

Something woke her. She blinked as she came to, surprised that she'd even been asleep. But the clock on the bedside table said it was one o'clock, which meant she must have been. She tried to parse what had woken her, then heard the bathroom door open. That was it — one of them must have gotten up.

As she lay there, footsteps echoed in the hallway. Definitely Peter. Far too heavy to be Martina, who liked to tiptoe through the house so that she could sneak up behind you and catch you doing something immoral, like looking at your reflection in the toaster oven. Vanity was one of her favorite sins. Or least favorite, depending on your perspective.

Peter's footsteps passed by her door and made it almost down the hallway before stopping. She waited for the sound of *his bedroom door opening and closing, but there was nothing. Instead, his footsteps resumed, coming back down the hallway.*

Maybe he'd forgotten something in the bathroom, she thought. She clung to that thought, ignoring the way her entire body had grown clammy and cold.

The doorknob twisted. She pulled the sheets up higher and snuggled down into the bed, pretending to be asleep. When the door opened, she kept her breathing nice and even. Just like as if she was asleep.

She could almost believe she was *asleep. It was easier that way. So when Peter closed the door behind him, when he crossed the room to her narrow bed, she told herself she was asleep. When he peeled back her blankets and gazed down at her form, clad only in a thin nightie, she was asleep. When he hoisted his hefty frame down on the bed beside her and took ahold of her hand, guiding it over himself, she was asleep.*

She was asleep, she was asleep, she was asleep.

NINETEEN

ON FRIDAY AFTERNOON, I arrive at the park about ten minutes before our scheduled meeting time. There's no sign of Taylor yet, so I sit on a bench to wait. I didn't think to bring a blanket or anything like that, but maybe it's too cold to sit on the ground, anyway. I did, however, bring a special treat from work: two freshly mixed servings of Ovaltine, poured into a couple of Donna's take-away milkshake cups. I figured Taylor would get a kick out of it.

While I wait, I amuse myself on my phone. I have a message from Enid, asking if I want to hang out tonight, but since I don't know how long Taylor and I will be together, I tell her I can't. I feel guilty and suggest tomorrow night instead. She shoots me a thumbs-up emoji in response.

I've already let my mother know not to expect me for dinner. She'd smiled and said it was fine, but I saw the pain flicker across her face. She still gets anxious in the house by herself. Or maybe it's knowing I'm out in the city alone. Most likely some combination of the two. I knew she wanted to say something — probably about the number of evenings I've been spending in the city lately — but she bit her tongue, as she almost always does.

I consider calling her to say hi and ask how she's doing, but I know the ringing phone sends her anxiety into overdrive, so it's probably better not to. But I have to do more to look out for her. I promise myself that I'll talk to Enid about the situation at our house. Maybe she, or even Heath or their mother, can check in on Mom every once in a while. Knowing there are people close by that she can call on if something happens might give her some peace of mind.

By the time I look up from my phone, I realize it's already a quarter past three. No sign of Taylor.

I send her a quick message letting her know I'm here. I wonder if I mixed up our meeting spot? The directions had been pretty clear, but she'd given them to me over the phone instead of texting, so it's possible I was misremembering. But no, I'm sure she said The Pool, the artificial pond off 102nd. That's where I am, parked on a bench, listening to the gently lapping water.

I wait for her to message me back, but my phone remains silent. The minutes tick by until it's half-past three and there's still no sign of her. I try calling, but she doesn't pick up. I don't bother leaving a message. I'm sure she'll be here any second.

But more minutes accrue, and still she doesn't appear. I sip at the Ovaltine, even though it tastes disgusting, and when I slurp up the last drops of it, I realize how long I've been sitting here. It's past four now. My ass is frozen from sitting on this bench, and the tops of my ears are about ready to snap off.

I'm annoyed now. Taylor has always tended to the flaky side of things, but she's never fully stood me up before. I send her a last message.

"Freezing my ass off. Heading home."

Just passive aggressive enough.

I half expect her to respond right away, because sometimes she replies as soon as she thinks I might genuinely be upset, but there's nothing. I shove my phone in my pocket, drop the two milkshake cups — one full, one empty — into the nearest trashcan, and stomp my way back to the street.

I suppose I could wait around the city to see if I hear from Taylor, but something about that rings too pathetic, even for me, so I go home to Staten Island. I pick up a pizza for my mother and me and text Enid to tell her I'm free tonight after all.

Mom seems happy to see me when I get home, and we eat our pizza in front of the television, yelling out answers to *Family Feud*.

"I'm going over to Enid's for a couple of hours," I tell her, once I've packed the leftovers into the fridge. "Do you need anything else?"

"Don't worry about me," she says, though she smiles grimly, since we both know the odds of that happening. "Say hello to her mother for me."

"I will." I can't remember the last time my mother wanted to say hello to anyone, even via a proxy.

I find Enid in her basement rec room, our usual spot for movie nights, arguing with Heath about whether *The Breakfast Club* beats *Ferris Bueller's Day Off* as the ultimate eighties movie.

"You guys, it's obviously *Dirty Dancing*," I say, happy to play peacemaker.

They both groan.

"Come on, Malice, you can't be serious."

"Yes, Death, I'm quite serious. Death-ly serious, you might say."

Enid snickers, and Heath rolls his eyes. "I don't know why I even bother trying with you two."

"Don't you have a date to go on?" I jab.

"No." His neck flushes and he glances away.

"Sorry," Enid says with a shrug. "She asked where you were the other day."

Heath mumbles something neither of us can make out, then takes the stairs two at a time, escaping the confines of the basement.

"Well, that was easier than expected." Enid flops down onto the couch and grabs the remote. "I was thinking *Blue Velvet*."

I'm not really in the mood for any David Lynch mindfucks. "Maybe something lighter?"

We settle on *The Princess Bride*, a favorite for both of us. We'd seen it in the theater in high school, when it was playing as a Saturday afternoon special feature. It might have even been a charity fundraiser, though I have no memory of what the charity was — but I remember vividly how happy I'd been to spend an afternoon in that dark theater with Enid, dreaming with our eyes open. Renata, her mother, had dropped us off, and we'd blown all our money on popcorn and candy and soda. Considering how limited my social life was in high school — and how hazardous my home life — that afternoon was one of the best I'd ever had. I feel a pang of gratefulness for my friendship with Enid. If it hadn't been for her, I would have had no one.

"Want to watch another one?" Enid offers when the movie ends.

"Sure. Let me just stretch and use the bathroom." I head upstairs, poking my nose into the kitchen for a minute, but neither Heath nor Renata are around. I use the washroom, washing my hands with fancy apricot-scented soap, and head back downstairs.

"Okay — so what's on tap next?" I ask.

Enid holds her phone up. "Don't you work at The Grant?"

"Yes," I say guiltily. Enid is another person who doesn't know I stopped working at the hotel weeks ago.

"They found a body there. Did you know that?"

"A body? What do you mean? Like—"

"Like, someone was killed there. They haven't said who or how. Just that they found a body. The news is saying the homicide team is there, so that sounds like murder to me."

I blanch. I have to grab onto the edge of the couch to keep from falling over. The news article may not have said who the body belonged to, but I know exactly who it is.

Weston Chambers.

That means I need to talk to Taylor. Now.

I perch on the edge of the sofa, legs shaking, and send a text message. All caps.

"WHAT DID YOU DO?"

TWENTY

MY MESSAGE to Taylor spins for a moment, and then small red type appears beneath it: ***Undelivered.***

Give me a damn break. I hit send a second time, but again, it spins and reads as undelivered.

"Fuck," I mutter.

"Everything okay?"

I startle; I'd forgotten Enid was even here. "Yeah, fine. I'm trying to get in touch with some girls I know from work. Just to make sure everyone's okay."

Enid nods and goes back to reading on her phone.

"I'm going to make a quick call," I tell her, already bounding up the stairs. I dart back into the kitchen, relieved to find that Heath and Renata are still nowhere to be seen. I dial Taylor's phone. My hands shake. I swallow; it's like sandpaper rubbing against Velcro.

The line clicks through, but a mechanical yet polite voice informs me that the number is no longer in service.

No. I slam the phone down on the counter.

Heath appears in the kitchen's doorway. "Oh, it's you. I thought something—" He pauses, regarding me. "Are you okay? You look like you've seen a ghost."

Not a ghost, I think. *Just a disappearing friend.*

"I got some bad news from work," I lie. It's amazing that the words fall, fully formed, from my mouth, that I'm still able to pull off an articulate sentence.

"Sorry. Anything I can do?"

"No, no. Thanks, but no. I just... I need to talk to Enid."

I bound back down the stairs to the basement. Enid puts her phone away. "Ready?"

"Enid, I'm so sorry. I have to go."

"What happened? What's wrong? You look sick."

I feel sick. "It's one of my friends at work. She's the one who found the body. She's really upset. I'm going to go sit with her."

Enid claps her hand over her mouth. "That's awful," she breathes. "I can't even imagine. Of course, you should go. We can finish this another time."

"Another time, for sure," I promise.

I stop over at my place to let Mom know I have to go back into the city.

"Alice, really? You're gone so much lately. And it's so late. Are you sure it's safe?"

"It's fine, Mom. I'll be fine. I promise." I'm practically hopping from foot to foot, I'm so eager to get out of there. Finally, I give her a quick kiss on the cheek and bounce back out of the house.

The entire ferry ride into the city, I keep trying Taylor, as if her number is going to suddenly reconnect, or my text messages are going to magically go through. It accomplishes nothing, of course, except for making me feel slightly more in control. Because otherwise I'd be standing on this ferry doing nothing and going completely out of my mind.

As soon as we hit land, I get a cab and go straight to Taylor's apartment building. I buzz her unit and wait.

"Come on, come on, come on," I mutter. There's no answer. I hit the buzzer again. I hit it over and over. I hold it down for so long that the buzzing sound starts to drive even me crazy.

Still no answer.

The door of the entrance flies open behind me and a group of drunk guys crowd in. One of them presses his pass against the electronic entry system, and the door beeps. I sneak in behind them. It's easy enough since they're drunk and far more interested in staring at my chest than noticing what I'm doing.

I go to the fourth floor and down the hall to Taylor's nondescript door. I knock, but there's no answer. I don't think she's here.

Still, that doesn't keep me from knocking so loud and so long that the neighbor across the hall finally sticks her head out her door. She's a tiny little thing, probably under five feet, and her silver hair is pulled back off her face, tucked inside some sort of kerchief. She wears a pink fleece robe and slippers.

"There's no one there," she says. "And you're keeping me up."

I ignore her and knock again, even though I know she's right. Taylor isn't here.

"You want me to call the cops?" she spits. "I'm going to call them." She waves around a huge phone, one of the old cordless varieties.

"I'm leaving," I mutter. I head to the elevator, but instead of going down, I get a flash of inspiration and hit the up button instead. The roof. Maybe she's on the roof.

I'm so excited by this idea that I practically run up the last set of stairs, pushing open the fire door in a burst of anticipation. But the roof is empty. The two patio chairs, where Taylor and I passed the evening last time, are still there, angled toward each other, but there's no one sitting in them.

I walk over to the edge of the roof and look out over the city. At the skyline that had so impressed me that first night, that had lured me into whatever web Taylor was spinning.

How did we get from there to here?

I know without a doubt that Weston Chambers is dead, and that Taylor killed him, exactly like she said she would. I don't know *why* she did it — mental illness? — but I know she did it. I also know that it has nothing to do with me, at least not really. She didn't do it because she cared about me, because she wanted revenge on my behalf. She barely knows me. Whatever she did, she did for her own reasons.

But knowing it intellectually is not the same as knowing it in my bones. I need to see her, to know this is for real, that she really killed him. I need to look her in the eye and ask her why.

I walk away from the edge of the roof and go back down

to the street. There's a small park across the road and a bench that's tagged with a few different graffiti symbols, white lines crisscrossing illegibly. I sit down, positioning myself so Taylor's building is in sight. From here I should be able to see when she comes home. I'll wait all night if I have to.

She can't avoid me forever.

TWENTY-ONE

I SIT on the bench in the park across from Taylor's apartment all night, but she never returns. Eventually the sun comes up, painting the sky in pink and then yellow and then blue, and still, there's no sign of her. I cross the street again and pull open the door of the building, half-heartedly buzzing her apartment. I know it's futile, though. She's not there. She didn't come home last night.

Wherever she is, it's not here.

Is she on the run? She disconnected her phone, so maybe she's scared to come back to the apartment, too. She'd been so sure that the police would have no reason to look at her for the murder, but maybe now that it's done, she's afraid. Now that it's real.

If she wants to hide, I can help her. If you're running from the law, what do you need more than anything else? You need money. You need to get far away — bus tickets, plane tickets, a place to stay. You probably even have to eventually change your name, but you need money for that, too.

And money is one thing I have.

Leaving Taylor's apartment, I walk to the nearest subway and ride back downtown. My bank is open on Saturdays, and there's no line, so within a few minutes, I'm holding a bigger wad of cash than I've ever held in my life. Ten thousand dollars. The teller had given me a funny look, but I had all the ID I needed. That money is mine. I *earned* it, I think morbidly.

The money is too conspicuous to carry around in my pocket, so the teller gives me a large yellow envelope. And even though getting mugged is pretty low on my list of concerns right now, as soon as I can, I buy a cheap black backpack and stuff the cash inside.

I don't know why I even want to help Taylor, but I do. Maybe it's because I share a sense of responsibility for what she's done. Maybe I just want to get her out of town as soon as possible. Because it also occurs to me that if she gets caught, there's nothing to stop her from telling the police that I asked her to do this. Maybe they'd even be able to charge me as an accessory, or a co-conspirator or something.

No, the best thing for everyone is if Taylor leaves town. The farther, the better. And if I can help her do that, I'm going to.

But even once I have the money, I still don't know how to contact Taylor. I could sit outside her apartment and wait for her, but for how long? And I don't know how else to get in touch with her. I don't know the name of the coffee shop where she works, so I can't go there. I can't look her up online, because I don't even know her last name.

God — I probably know more about her roommate than I do about her. What a mess.

Inspiration hits me. The roommate. I don't know Taylor's last name, but I know Sarah's. I still have the program from that play, *The Haunting of Liliane Flowers*. It's at home on my desk in my bedroom, tucked into my copy of *The Catcher In The Rye*, the only book we read in high school that I actually liked.

But I don't even need the program, I realize. I use my phone to search for the play and find a few different mentions of it, including a Facebook page. The page has bios of all the actors, including — there she is — Sarah Constantine.

Unfortunately, while Sarah has a personal Facebook page, it's pretty locked down, and she has her profile set so that she can't get messages from strangers. I add her as a friend, but I'm not hopeful that she'll accept my request in time, if at all.

I go back to the play's page and check out the dates of the run. For once, luck is on my side — their last show is tonight.

Even though I'm falling asleep on my feet, I decide to stay in the city. It's already past noon, and it would be pointless to go home to the island only to come back in time for the show. Not to mention that if I let myself go home, the only thing I'll want to do is crawl into bed, and if I do that, I might not wake up for three days.

So instead of going home, I go to the library. It only takes me another ten minutes to get there, and when I do, I'm immediately greeted by the familiar faces of Patience and Fortitude, the two lions who guard the building. Stepping inside, I look around Astor Hall. It never fails to thrill me. This is the New York life of my fantasies. The life I've dreamed of for so long.

The life I'll never have.

I wander through the hall to the Rose Main Reading Room and let myself be awed, as I try to temporarily put Taylor and Weston from my mind. I weave among the shelves, my footsteps echoing slightly, the leather sleeves of my jacket brushing lightly against my body and making a swishing noise that echoes obscenely in the quiet. The library is busy, as it always is, with a good mix of students, tourists, and loners like me. I'm anonymous in there, invisible. Just the way I like it.

I kill a couple of hours wandering through the shelves, but I'm so tired that I can barely keep my eyes open. I get a stack of architecture and design books to flip through and take them to a table away from the worst of the foot traffic. I stick the backpack between my feet, looping the straps under the legs of my chair so that no one can snatch it without my notice. I crack open a book and start flipping through the pages — I swear I do — but after a few minutes, my eyes are so heavy that I put my head on the desk and let them close.

I wake up with a start just as the library is about to close. My mouth is so dry I wonder if I've been licking the pages of the open book in front of me while I slept. My head aches, and my skin feels too hot. Flushed.

Automatically, I reach for my phone. I try to text Taylor again, and I try calling her, too. Like before, neither the message nor the call goes through. Those avenues are dead.

But I'm going to see Sarah soon. Sarah will know where

she is. Maybe I can even get her to let me into their apartment so I can wait for Taylor there.

Before I put my phone away, I Google The Grant and hit the news tab to see if there's any new information on the body.

Even though I'd been expecting it, all the blood drains from my face when I see the headline:

Hotel Death Confirmed as Weston Chambers.

The headline on the story below it is even more salacious.

Wealthy Playboy Dead In Grizzly Slaying.

I scan the articles, but there still aren't a lot of details. They discovered the body Friday evening. Police are treating it as a homicide but haven't yet revealed the exact cause of death. The hotel isn't commenting. The Chambers family isn't commenting.

A man in a uniform approaches, and I quickly close out of the browser. A cop? Already? I back out of my seat before realizing it's not a cop but a library security guard.

"Library's closing, miss. You'll have to leave now."

But I've already gathered up my backpack and am scurrying out of the Rose Room.

When I get to The Black Spot, they won't let me in without a ticket. When I try to buy one, the guy working the front door rolls his eyes.

"All sold out," he sneers. He's wearing a black wool hat, rolled up so it doesn't cover his ears, and a pair of round glasses with clear plastic frames. His pants look too tight to sit down in. "Didn't you see the review in *The Village Voice*? They called us 'riveting and deep as the ocean.'"

I resist the urge to snort. "Look, I don't need to see the show. I just need to speak to one of the actors. Sarah Constantine."

"Sarah's in pre-show mode right now," he says. "She can't be disturbed."

Of course, she can't. "Can I see her after the show?"

"You can try," Glasses says. "But I doubt you'll be able to find her. She's going to be at the cast party with the others. Why don't you give her the night to herself? Talk to her tomorrow. Unless," he pauses, considering me. "Are you press?"

"No, but I—"

He turns away. "Then you can get in touch with her on your own time."

I mentally kick myself. I should have agreed with him. Yes, I'm press, and I want to write about your shitty little show.

I stand outside the building while the audience files in through the single door. The line this time is even longer than it was when Taylor and I were here.

Once everyone is inside, I consider sneaking in, but the asshole working the front of house locks the doors behind him when he goes in. I'm pretty sure that's some kind of horrific fire code violation, but there's nothing else I can do here. I spot a cafe across the street and head there, where I grab a seat near the window. I get an extra-extra large Americano and wait, my eyes never leaving The Black Spot across the street.

Two and a half hours later, the first people stream out into the street. Some of them leave, but many of them stay crowded around the building in small groups, smoking cigarettes and surfing on their phones and discussing the 'piece of art' they just witnessed.

I try to push in through the now unlocked door, but the same guy from earlier blocks my passage.

"The show's over," he says.

"I need to talk to Sarah," I remind him.

"She's in post-show mode. She needs to decompress."

Jesus. No wonder Taylor used to roll her eyes at this woman. I try to push my way in, but Glasses isn't having it. We're drawing the attention of the other lingering show-goers, and the last thing I want is attention, so I back off.

There's an alley that runs alongside the building next to The Black Spot, so I decide to wait there. Maybe I can catch Sarah when she comes out.

But it's cold and I'm restless and the alley smells like pee. I pace back and forth along it, first to the street and then back into the darkness. Eventually, I realize the end of this alley intersects with another alley, one which leads behind the row of buildings containing the theater.

I duck into the adjoining alley. Maybe I'll get lucky and The Black Spot has a back door. I could try to sneak in that way.

When the building comes into view, lit by a single exterior light caged in a metal fixture, I find that The Black Spot does, indeed, have a back door, and right now it's propped open with a brick. A dark-haired woman huddles over an e-cigarette. The smell of sour apple reaches my nose.

"Sarah?"

She jerks. She peers suspiciously into the darkness. "Who's there?"

I step into the light. "Sorry, I didn't mean to scare you. I was hoping we could talk."

"Who are you?" She pulls her jacket tighter. She's wearing a red quilted puffer coat, but underneath she's still got on the long white nightdress she wore in the show. Her face is thick with stage makeup, but up close I can tell she's much older than I'd thought. Mid-thirties, maybe almost forty.

"My name's Alice. I'm a friend of Taylor's."

Her expression doesn't change. She takes in another long breath from the vaping device.

"I was wondering if you knew how I could get in touch with her."

"Who?"

"Taylor."

"Taylor who?"

I flush. "I don't know her last name. Your roommate."

"My roommate?" She barks out a laugh. "My 'roommate' is my husband, and his name's not Taylor."

Husband? No, Taylor had said she had a boyfriend. But maybe she was confused about that. "I mean Taylor. The blonde girl. You share an apartment with her in Hell's Kitchen."

Sarah shakes her head. She clicks off the e-cigarette and stuffs it into her pocket. "Like I said, I don't know any Taylor.

I live with my husband in a townhouse in Brooklyn. And his name's Brandon, not Taylor."

"You don't live in Hell's Kitchen?"

"I've never lived in Hell's Kitchen."

"The big apartment building on 10th Avenue? With the beige walls. The rooftop?"

She shakes her head. "Nope. Sorry."

My stomach bottoms out. *What the hell is going on?*

TWENTY-TWO

WHILE I STAND THERE, dumbfounded, Sarah pockets her e-cigarette and turns back to the building.

"Wait!" I call out. I can't let her walk away. I fumble for my phone. "Here. This is her picture. You know her, right?"

Sarah takes the phone and studies the picture. She shakes her head. "Nope. Sorry."

"No," I say, still holding out the phone. "No, no, no. You know her. She's your roommate. I don't know why she told you to lie to me, but—"

"I'm not lying to you." She bristles.

"Dominic," I blurt. "Is Dominic still here? He knows her, too."

Sarah considers me. "Yeah, he's still here."

"Can we talk to him?"

Instead of answering, she walks back into the building, up the small flight of stairs into the back door. I follow close behind. I'm not letting her out of my sight. I don't want her to get to Dominic before I do. Whatever's going on, I know Sarah's somehow involved.

She leads me to a small green room, packed with stuff. Furniture, and clothes, and spare lights, and a dozen of the same metal folding chairs that stood in the audience, folded and stacked against one wall. A handful of people are still in the room, passing around a bottle of champagne. I recognize most of them as actors from the show, and I figure the others are part of the crew. Dominic is in the center, his arm slung around a petite brunette in a skin-tight red dress.

"Dominic," Sarah says. "This lady wants to talk to you."

Dominic looks over and raises his eyebrows. His petite brunette friend narrows hers. Dominic saunters over.

"Are you a fan?"

"No. I mean, yes," I correct when a frown creeps onto his face. He's much shorter up close than he appeared on stage. Stalkier, too. He's got a musculature that wasn't visible underneath the billowy shirt he wore in the show, but which is readily apparent now that he's stripped down to a plain t-shirt. "I'm trying to get in touch with Taylor. You used to go out with her."

He rubs his hand over his chin. "I don't remember a Taylor. Then again, there have been a lot of girls..." He flashes a grin at Sarah, who rolls her eyes.

I thrust my phone out to him. "This is her. Blonde, pretty, loud."

He studies the picture and shakes his head. "I don't know. Like I said, there have been a lot of girls, but she doesn't look familiar. Not saying I didn't maybe sleep with her at some point, but she was definitely never my girlfriend."

He lowers his voice, glancing over his shoulder at his lady friend, who's still glowering at us. "I don't really do girlfriends, if you know what I mean."

"Come on, people," a voice calls from the doorway. Great — Glasses is back. He claps his hands together. "Red Rooster in ten minutes. First round's on me."

They all shuffle past me, laughing and chattering, still on a high from their show. When the brunette in the red dress goes by, she makes sure to bump hard against my shoulder.

I follow them wordlessly outside, only because there's no point in standing there anymore. There are no answers here.

Taylor is more of a mystery than ever.

———

After the play's crew are all gone, I go home. I have nothing else to do. No other leads. No way to find Taylor.

I don't even know who she is anymore. Had she lied about having a roommate? Or is Sarah the one lying? I don't know what motivation Sarah would have to lie to me, but I don't know what reason Taylor would have, either. None of it makes any sense.

By the time I get home, my mother is in bed, though the light in her bedroom is still on, shining out from beneath the door. For a moment, I consider knocking on the door, going into her room and crawling into bed with her, the same way I had after Dad died. That first week, we'd spent every night curled up together, mindlessly watching late-night infomercials and sleeping in fits. Even though our life was arguably better without him in it, the sudden shock of his absence had left us both stunned.

Then I started to wonder about the timing of it. How convenient it was that he had died now, just two weeks after Mom had said, "Enough is enough." Just two weeks after she'd become steely with composure.

As soon as the notion wormed its way into my mind, I retreated to my own room, my own bed. Mom slept alone — or didn't. Her anxiety got worse. My misanthropy kicked into overdrive. We were citizens of two different countries, an ocean of unspoken truths between us.

That's how I feel again now.

I stand outside her door for a good five minutes, wanting to go in but hesitating. I hear her rustling the bedsheets, and for a second, I think maybe she knows I'm standing here, maybe she's going to come and open the door. Instead, the bedside light clicks off and the crack of illumination under the door disappears.

I go to my room and climb into bed, still wearing my jeans. I don't think I'm going to sleep, but I fall into darkness as soon as my feet lift off the floor.

In the morning, things still look bleak. Taylor is gone. Weston is dead. Two unarguable facts. Nothing I can do about it.

But I'm still at loose ends. I can't let this go. I have to know what she did, and more importantly, why she did it. Why lie about Sarah and Dominic? Or, alternately, why get them to lie to me? It nags at the back of my consciousness. It's an itch, and the only thing that will scratch it is answers.

And the only person who can give me answers is Taylor.

After inhaling a couple of slices of leftover pizza and half a pot of coffee, I decide to head back into the city. The only solid lead I have is Taylor's apartment. I know she really lived there, because I visited the place myself. I ate dinner there, I spent the night there. It's real. So someone there has to know her. The neighbor across the hall, the silver-haired lady with the pink robe and the cordless phone — surely, she must know Taylor. Maybe she even knows her last name. And if that fails, maybe I could try the property manager. They'll at least have Taylor's last name, maybe an emergency contact number. I don't know how I'll get them to divulge that information, but I decide to worry about that when I get there.

More motivated, I ride the ferry into the city and go straight to Taylor's apartment building. I buzz her apartment half-heartedly, not expecting a response, but a second after I take my finger off the buzzer, the light flashes and the door clicks as it unlocks.

Stunned, I yank it open before it can lock again. *Taylor.* She's actually home. I wait impatiently for the elevator and ride up to the fourth floor, then run down the hallway until I get to her door.

"Taylor!" I pound onthe door. "Taylor, it's me."

The door swings open a second later. I jolt in surprise at the figure standing there. It isn't Taylor, but a guy. He's my age, maybe. Asian, tall and thin. Handsome, in a clean-cut sort of way. He's wearing a grey t-shirt and yellow rubber gloves that cover the bottom half of his arms, right up to the elbows.

"Can I help you?" His voice is smooth, even. Just the slightest hint of a New York accent.

"Who are you?" I blurt.

"Paul. Who are you?"

"I'm looking for Taylor."

"Sorry. There's no one here right now."

"I'll wait for her."

"Sorry, you misunderstand. No one is staying here right now. There's no one to wait for."

"No, that's wrong. Taylor stays here. She lives here. This is her apartment."

He shakes his head. "No, she doesn't. And no, it isn't."

"She does. I was here... We had..." I look around the apartment, at the blues and beiges, at the kitchen where we'd cooked together. "We had spaghetti. And cupcakes."

"I'm sure you did," he says. "But she doesn't live here. This is a vacation rental. And it's currently unoccupied. I'm getting it ready for the next guests."

A vacation rental? No. That can't be right. Taylor lives here. She lives here with Sarah, and they...

But details are clicking into place. The bland decor. The bare essentials in the cupboards. The Goldman Sachs mug. The fact that Taylor didn't know where anything was.

It's all been a lie. Everything Taylor ever told me was a lie — right down to the apartment she never really lived in.

TWENTY-THREE

"COULD I HAVE A DRINK OF WATER?" I whisper. I don't trust my voice. My skin is too hot, too tight.

Paul eyes me suspiciously, but walks to the kitchen and fills a drinking glass with tap water.

"You don't look so good," he says when he hands it to me.

Instead of answering, I finish the glass in one swallow and collapse down onto the brown sofa. The same one I'd crashed on the first night I met Taylor, after we'd drank whiskey on the roof and I'd confided in her about the rape.

Paul stares down at me, concerned. I'm not sure if that concern is for me or for his sofa. "You aren't going to be sick, are you?"

"You ever feel like you're going crazy?" When he doesn't answer, I sit up. "Can you tell me the name of the last person who rented this place?"

"No, sorry. Guest info is confidential."

"Please. I really need to find this girl. She... took something from me, and I really need to get it back."

"What did she take?"

My sanity. "Something valuable."

"I'm not responsible for any theft, you know."

"It's not about that. I just need to track her down."

"I don't think I should give out that information. Maybe if you email the head office. They have lawyers and stuff."

I can't go through lawyers and stuff. What am I going to tell them? *A girl pretended to be my friend and maybe killed someone and I'd really like to find her so I can figure out what the fuck is going on?* Not a very compelling argument. And not one that makes me sound particularly sane, either.

"Please." I'm not above begging. I'm also not above bribery. "I can pay you."

His eyebrows shoot up. "That's not... I mean, I still shouldn't."

"Please. A thousand dollars."

"A thousand—"

"Two thousand. Cash. I can give it to you right now. All you have to do is tell me who rented this place. Do you have contact info?"

"Yes, but—"

But I'm already unzipping my backpack. I pull open the manila envelope and count out twenty crisp hundred-dollar bills. I wave them in front of Paul's face. "Easy money," I say. "All I need is some info. No one will ever even know you gave it to me."

He swallows, but his eyes never leave the cash.

"Let me get my phone," he says eventually.

He peels off the rubber gloves as he goes to the kitchen and grabs his phone off the island. A bottle of cleaning spray and a roll of paper towels stand at the ready. At the back of my mind, I think about evidence — fingerprints, hairs, DNA. I could ask him to stop cleaning, call the police and tell them my suspicions. But I already know I won't. I keep my mouth shut and wait until Paul comes back to the living room.

"You're really just going to give me that cash? This isn't a trick?"

"It's not a trick." I thrust the money at him. "It's yours."

He takes it gingerly, as if he's afraid I might sucker punch him when he reaches for it or something. He hastily stuffs it into his pocket and taps the screen of his phone.

"The last guest was here for four weeks. She had it booked for six, but when she asked to be let out of her agreement early, I agreed. I never have any problems filling this place." He shrugs at his own humblebrag.

"Right, right." Come on. Just give me a name. A phone number. Maybe an address.

He peers down at the screen. "The guest's name was Alice Brewster."

The drinking glass falls out of my hand. It connects with the glass coffee table before it hits the laminate flooring below, shattering into a thousand pieces.

"Shit, look what you did." Paul's already rushing to the kitchen, grabbing a small hand broom and a dustbin.

"Alice Brewster?" I sputter. "Did you say Alice Brewster? That can't be right."

"Yup. It's right." He kneels and starts sweeping up the shattered glass around my feet.

I glare at him. "Do you really just let people use whatever

name they want to check in with? What kind of shady business is this?"

"It's not at all," he says. "All guests have to provide proof of their identity. Alice submitted a scan of her driver's license." He inspects the coffee table to see if the glass damaged it.

"That's impossible."

Satisfied that the coffee table is unharmed, he stands and takes the dustbin of glass shards to the trash. "It's not. I have it right here."

He strides back over and holds the phone out in front of me. I stare at the screen in disbelief. There it is. My picture, my address. My license.

My stomach is a koi pond, with too many fish darting around in it. "Does anything about that photo look familiar?" I say through gritted teeth.

He looks at it again, and then at me. "Wait, that's you. Is that you?"

"Ding ding ding."

"So you rented this place? Why'd you pay me two thousand dollars to tell you that?"

I close my eyes against the stupid. "I didn't. Somebody must have created a fake account in my name."

"Ohhhh. But that's not..." he blinks. "Hey, you can't hold me responsible for that. I did everything I was required to do as a host. I can't control whether or not someone's using a fake identity."

"I don't care about that." I can't guarantee him that the police won't, not after they start looking into Weston's murder, but I don't bother mentioning that. "Is there anything else at all you can tell me about the person who stayed here? Do you log IP addresses or anything like that?" Not that I would know how to track an IP address, but at least it would be something, and that's more than I have right now.

"Nothing like that, no. Again, maybe the head office would have that information, but not the hosts."

"What about when she stayed here? Do you have security cameras? Does the building?"

"No cameras inside. It's a privacy issue. The building has one in the lobby, but I'm not sure it even works. I think it might be a decoy."

And even if it isn't, I don't know how I'll get my hands on it, or even what good it would do if I could.

"Was there a phone number?"

"Yes," he says, seeming happy to provide me with an affirmative at last. He rattles off the number. It's the same one Taylor has been texting me from, the one that's now disconnected.

"How did she pay? She must have had a credit card."

"Yes, but we don't get access to the numbers. Again, you might want to try—"

"The head office. I get it."

"Sorry." He touches his pocket, as if he's afraid I might ask for my money back.

"It's fine," I say, even though it's not. I have no idea how to find Taylor now. This was my last hope, and it's a dead end.

"Is that all?" He heads back to the kitchen, picking up the

bottle of cleaning spray. He probably just wants to get rid of me. I can't say I blame him.

"One more thing," I ask as I make my way to the door. "What date did she check in?"

He checks his phone, again scrolling and tapping. "The last weekend of September."

The last weekend of September. That would have been a few days before I met her for the first time at El Diablo's. Either that was one hell of a coincidence... or it wasn't a coincidence at all.

And given the fact that she already had my license at that point, I'm going to go with the latter.

I leave Taylor's apartment — or should I say, Paul's apartment — and go straight to the ferry. I have nothing else to do in the city. There are no other leads, no other avenues to pursue. Taylor's in the wind. If she was ever even there to begin with.

That thought is like a scalpel slicing the palm of my hand. It's so simple, a slim incision, but as I watch, the blood seeps from it, filling my mind.

What if Taylor was never there to begin with? What if I made her up?

I go over the facts, or at least the things I consider to be 'the facts.' I met Taylor at a bar. No one else I know met her. She claimed to have a job working at The Grant, yet she wasn't on the schedule and Minnie had no idea who she was. The apartment she lived in was rented by me, or by someone using my ID. Her supposed roommate and ex-boyfriend don't know who she is. Her phone number is not in service.

And most importantly, she killed Weston Chambers, the man who ruined my life.

What's more likely — that a real person did all this, for no apparent reason? Or that I somehow made it all up? Could my broken brain have manufactured Taylor as some kind of alter ego? After all, she was everything I wanted to be — brave, beautiful, bold. She lived life while I hid from it. She took action while I remained stuck, inert.

She did the thing I'd been dreaming of doing for so long, ever since the day of the attack. She'd wiped Weston Chambers from the face of the earth. Made him pay, at last, for what he did to me.

But did she do it? Or did I?

As we arrive on Staten Island and I disembark from the ferry, another thought comes to me — the photo. I have a picture of Taylor on my phone. I whip it out right away, as if seeing it will reassure me I'm not crazy. As I scroll through the photos, I have a sinking feeling that I won't be able to find it, that I'll have dreamed up that, too.

But no, there it is. I hold the phone up triumphantly and then glance around, embarrassed. No one's paying me any attention, though. To them, I'm not a crazy person but just another young woman, coming home from a job in the city.

I study the picture. There she is. Blonde, bold, beautiful Taylor.

But is it really her? The photo isn't the best quality. Her eyes are closed, her face blurred as she moved her head. The background is mostly dark, punctuated with streaks of neon, light leaks that make the photo look feverish and frenetic. We'd been at Karnival — or at least I had. Maybe I had taken the photo of some random girl, out with her friends for a night of dancing.

I don't want to believe it, but my mind flits back and forth across the idea. There's merit to it. Weight. Maybe I'm really going crazy.

Nausea tightens my throat. I try to breathe and focus on making it home without throwing up.

By the time I trudge up the street toward my house, I'm ready to climb into bed and sleep straight through to tomorrow. Or next year. Maybe I'll wake up and find that all of this is just a bad dream.

But as I get closer to home, I see something that makes my blood run cold. Parked in front of our house is a police cruiser. Memories of my father's death come rushing back at me. The officers at the door, my mother's face, pale and drawn.

As I throw myself at the front door of our house, I only have one thought.

Mom.

TWENTY-FOUR

I BURST INTO THE HOUSE, already yelling. "Mom? Mom! Are you okay? What happened?"

"Alice, please." Her voice comes from the living room, measured and clear. Only a hint of the usual anxiety. "We're in the living room."

I step into the room and find my mother tucked into her usual spot on the corner of the couch. With her are two men who look out of place in our overly floral living room, and comically oversized for the tiny chintz chairs they're perched on. They aren't even overly large men, it's just that the chairs are stupidly small.

Neither of them are wearing uniforms, but they read immediately as cops.

"These detectives would like to speak to you," Mom says, confirming my suspicion. She sounds normal, but I can tell by the way her hands twist in her lap that she's more upset than she's letting on.

"Hello, Alice," one of them says, standing. "My name is

Detective Douglas. This is my partner, Detective Vyas. We just want to ask you a few questions, like your mother said. Is that okay with you?"

I figure I don't have much choice in the matter, so I nod and sit on the sofa next to my mother. "What's this about?"

"Did you formerly work at The Grant Hotel?" Detective Douglas starts. He's the larger of the two, a muscular white man with curiously small lips.

"Yes," I whisper.

Mom shifts beside me, and I cringe. I know she's noted the word 'formerly'.

"How long did you work there?"

"I started a little over two years ago."

"And when did you stop?"

I close my eyes for a second, grimly aware of my mother's presence beside me. "About six weeks ago."

My mother doesn't react, but I know she's processing the information.

"I see. And what was the reason you stopped working there?"

"It was a... mutually agreed-upon decision."

"Does that mean you quit? Or were you fired?"

"I guess I quit."

"You guess?"

I shrug. There really isn't a better explanation for what happened, unless I give them the whole sordid story, and no way do I want to do that with my mother sitting beside me, wringing her hands as if there were a dishtowel between them. I'll keep that part private for as long as I can.

"Did you sign an agreement with the hotel upon your departure?"

"An agreement?"

"Yes. Was there any kind of agreement reached between yourself and the hotel?"

"Yes." Shit. Maybe they already know everything.

"And what did that agreement entail?"

I don't answer. I can't get into this right now. I can't. Are they looking at me as a suspect? If they know what Weston did to me, they'd know I had reason to want him dead.

"We'll come back to that," says Detective Vyas, cutting in for the first time. He's smaller than his partner, with dark skin and ears that stick out a little too far. But his suit is nicer, a trendier slim cut. His voice is soothing. "When were you last at The Grant?"

"August 24. My last day of work there."

"So you haven't been back at all since then?"

"No, sir."

"You weren't there on Wednesday? Wednesday of this week?"

My neck flushes. "Oh. That."

"Yes, Ms. Brewster. That. Were you there this week?"

"Briefly. I was in the neighborhood, and I really had to pee. I mean, like *really*. It was an emergency. I ducked in to use the facilities, and then I left again," I say, hoping that he hasn't spoken to Minnie. I'm guessing prissy Eldon is the one who told them I was there.

"I see," he says. "And were you there again after that?"

"No."

"Were you there on Friday?"

"Friday? No."

"You're sure?"

"Positive."

He makes a note of something. Detective Douglas jumps in again.

"What's your relationship with Weston Chambers?"

I blanch. "I don't have a relationship with him."

"But you know him?"

"Not really. I mean, I know *of* him. He was a guest at the hotel sometimes. And he's in the news a lot."

"So you never had any contact with him?"

I don't answer again. My stomach is roiling. I'm going to be sick.

Because it's clear that they think I killed Weston. At the very least, they're considering the possibility. They think I was angry about what he did to me, and that maybe I went in there on Friday afternoon and killed him.

And the worst part is, I don't know if they're wrong.

"Can you tell us where you were Friday afternoon, between the hours of two and five?"

"I worked until two."

"Where do you work?"

"At a restaurant, a diner, called Donna's. In midtown."

"Okay." He makes another notation. "You worked until two, and then what did you do?"

"I went to Central Park. I was supposed to meet a friend for a picnic."

"So you were with a friend? Until what time?"

"No, I was *supposed* to meet her. She never showed up."

"Why not?"

"I don't know. I... haven't been able to get ahold of her since then." My hands are shaking. I clench them into fists, hoping neither detective has noticed.

"So what you're saying is that you were alone during that time? In Central Park?"

"Yes."

"No one saw you?"

"Not that I'm aware of. There were other people around, but I doubt anyone noticed me. I don't know any of them."

"I see. How long were you in the park?"

"Till about four thirty. Then I took the ferry home."

"How'd you get from the park to the ferry?"

"I walked to 103rd Street and then took the subway to South Ferry Station."

"All right." The two detectives exchange a glance. My stomach drops another inch.

"Ms. Brewster, are you aware that Weston Chambers is dead?"

I swallow. "I saw it on the news."

"That's how you knew? You saw it on the news?"

"Yes." I jut my chin out.

"And that's all you know about his death?"

"Yes."

I consider telling them about Taylor. The words are on the tip of my tongue. But how can I expect them to believe me when I don't even know what to believe myself? The story sounds absurd.

"Were you aware that Weston Chambers was murdered?"

I swallow. "Yes," I whisper.

"Would you consent to providing your fingerprints? For elimination purposes, you understand. We're looking at everyone who may have been in Mr. Chambers' suite, and as you worked at The Grant and have cleaned that room in the past, we'd like to rule out your prints."

I hesitate. For the first time — maybe ever — I look to my mother for guidance. Am I supposed to say yes? Do I have to say yes? Is it worse if I don't?

Beside me, my mother is as tense as a coiled spring. "Detectives, my daughter has been very helpful, but you're clearly distressing her."

"We're investigating a murder, ma'am."

"I understand that. But I also know that you can't go around haranguing citizens. If you'd like my daughter's fingerprints, you'll need a court order. Now I'll kindly ask you to leave our home."

Detectives Douglas and Vyas exchange a look.

"Now, please." My mother stands, brooking no argument.

The two detectives stand as well. I'm the only one still sitting, and I feel childlike and small. My mother shows the detectives to the door.

"It's in your best interest to help us, Ms. Brewster," Detective Douglas says. "Both of you." He casts a glance back at me, and I shrivel even more under his stony stare.

"Goodbye, detectives." My mother opens the door and ushers them out, letting the door slam shut behind them.

"Mom, that was..."

She collapses onto the chintz chair just vacated by Detective Vyas. She's shaking, trembling from head to toe.

"Mom, are you okay?" I stand over her. Her skin looks clammy and cold.

"I just need — could you make me a cup of tea?"

"Of course." I hurry to the kitchen and set the kettle on the stove. While it slowly boils, I ready the tea bags in cups, then return to the living room, eying my mother nervously. She flashes me a weak smile.

"Your father taught me that," she says. "You can't let them walk all over you. You give an inch and they'll take every last one of your civil liberties."

"That sounds like him." I don't have a lot of fond memories of my father, but for once, his paranoia has come in handy. "He was the first person I thought of when I saw the police car outside. I thought of that night."

"Me, too," she admits. "I thought they had finally..." She trails off as the kettle in the kitchen shrieks.

My stomach dips. She thought they were here for *her*. That they'd finally figured out what she'd done.

"Alice, the tea."

"Right." I return to the kitchen where I make us both cups of milky Earl Grey and bring them to the living room. We sit in silence for a few minutes, sipping from our steaming cups.

Eventually Mom says, "Do you want to tell me what that was about? Who's Weston Chambers?"

I shrug, blowing on my tea in order to avoid her gaze. "He was just this guy who used to go to the hotel. He got killed, I guess."

"And why would they want to talk to you about that?"

"I don't know." I still won't look at her.

"Did you lose your job at The Grant? You could have told me, you know."

"I know." I shrug again. "I guess I didn't want you to worry."

"You know that's going to happen, regardless." Mom cracks a smile, and I have to grin in return.

"Fair enough."

"Did this Weston person have something to do with the reason you lost your job?"

"Sort of. It's a long story." I really don't want to get into it, and I especially don't want to get into it with my mother.

"You can tell me, you know."

But I shake my head. My mother has already shouldered enough in her life, the last thing I want to do is saddle her with any of this.

That's why I need to find Taylor. I need to figure out what the hell is going on before things really blow up.

TWENTY-FIVE

IN THE MORNING, I feel like I have a hangover, despite drinking nothing stronger than Earl Grey the night before. I pop a couple of painkillers and make an enormous pot of coffee, which I consume in its entirety before grabbing my backpack and pulling on my boots.

"You're going out?" Mom asks. "Again?"

"I have to work today. At the diner. Donna's."

"All right. But promise me you'll come right home when you're done."

"I will." The lie comes easily. I have no intention of coming straight home; I have something else I want to do after work. Something I need to do.

My shift at Donna's goes about as well as usual. I'll never be a people person, but I'm a surprisingly good waitress. I have a good memory, and I can handle more tables than even some of the more experienced servers there. What do you know, I think bitterly, as I juggle bottles of ketchup and fresh pots of coffee and clean cutlery and stacks and stacks and stacks of dirty plates — maybe I've found my calling.

When my shift is over, I change out of my uniform and head back out into the crisp air. Donna's is in Midtown, just a few blocks from The Grant, but I take a circuitous route to get there, walking all the way around Bryant Park and coming up on the hotel from a direction that's opposite what I'd usually take. I stay on the other side of the street until I'm right in front of the grandiose hotel. I don't dare go any closer in case Eldon or someone from Security sees me.

I'd been expecting crime scene tape, police cruisers parked outside, but there's no sign that anything happened here on Friday. The Grant looks as pristine and unsullied as it always has. Perhaps only Weston's suite is still marked off. And maybe not even that. I'm sure The Grant's management wasted no time in ensuring everything returned to normal as quickly and efficiently as possible. They're experts at sweeping things under the rug. I know that better than anyone.

I head back the way I came and turn left at the next intersection, crossing the street and looping around to the block behind The Grant. The service entrance is on this street, and this is where the housekeeping staff enter and exit. It's the entrance I used to use. There's a stone half-wall that runs along the opposite side of the street, sectioning off a parking lot that serves the government offices up the street and overflow from the hotel's underground parking. I park my ass there and wait. It's only three o'clock, and the day shift doesn't end until four, but I don't want to risk missing her.

The air is frigid, and I wish I'd brought gloves. I blow on

my fingers to keep them warm. My ass goes numb, and I pace back and forth along a narrow section of the wall.

At almost exactly four, the service door opens and a couple of women breeze out. One of them lights up a cigarette before the door even swings closed behind her. They come in waves after that — all women, mostly young, in groups of two or three, huddled in puffy jackets pulled tight against the cold.

By four thirty, I haven't seen her, and I'm worried that maybe I missed her or that she has the day off. Then the door opens and Minnie slips out.

She's by herself, thank God. Her pale blue parka is open, revealing a white sweatshirt and jeans. She's looking at something on her phone and not paying any attention to her surroundings.

"Minnie!" I call, rushing across the street and almost getting rammed by an irate cabbie.

She jumps. "Alice, you scared me."

"Sorry. Do you have a few minutes to talk?"

She checks the time on her phone. "A few minutes. If I'm not on the train by quarter to five, I miss the bus, and if I miss the bus, I have to wait another hour for the next one."

"I won't keep you long. Let me buy you a tea."

"I haven't seen your friend," she says as we walk. "Taylor. I'd have called you if I had."

"That's okay," I say, although disappointment pricks me like a pin. If Minnie had seen Taylor, that would at least confirm that I hadn't imagined her.

We duck into a coffee shop, and I buy us both cups of tea.

We don't bother sitting down, but head back outside and stroll toward the subway station.

"I heard about what happened last week," I say as soon as we're outside again. "The murder."

"Oh my," Minnie says, shaking her head. "What a stir. Never seen anything like it in my life."

"Do you know what happened?"

"Not really. It was Dina and Olga P. who found the body. They're both very upset. Off work all week."

I make supportive noises. I can see how the act of finding a dead body could be traumatic, but I'm here for information.

"Have you heard anything about what happened?"

Minnie shakes her head. "The police say nothing. I've been checking the news every day."

"What about unofficially?" I know that no matter how quiet people try to keep things, word always gets around. Especially in a place like The Grant.

She hesitates, sipping her tea. "Dina said it was very bloody. They stabbed him, you know. I don't know how many times. She said there was blood everywhere in the room. She said it was awful."

Even without seeing it, my stomach turns at the thought. Had Taylor done that?

Had I?

"What about the investigation? Do the police have any suspects?"

"Oh, I don't know, Alice."

"But what's the gossip mill saying? Come on, you must know something." Is the desperation evident in my voice? I try to tone it down. "I know it's none of my business. But the police were at my house yesterday. I think they think I'm a suspect. Because of... because of what happened. With Weston."

"Oh, poor Alice," Minnie says. She bows her head. "Poor, poor Alice. I'm sorry. We don't hear much. Dina said there was a knife in the room. She saw it. Right on the bed beside him. And Eldon says they were able to get fingerprints off the knife. They're just trying to match them."

I don't bother asking how in the hell Eldon knows this, because I have no doubt that, somehow, he does. He always made it his business to know everything that was going on in the hotel. He knew more about the business of most celebrities, politicians, and athletes than their own handlers probably did. So I doubt police business is enough to elude him.

But this also makes me think differently about the excuse the detectives made when they came to see me yesterday. They'd said they wanted my prints only to exclude me as someone who'd been in the room before. But if they had a knife, and if they'd been able to get prints off that knife, that meant they were trying to nail down the culprit.

If I'd consented to give my fingerprints yesterday, would they have been a match?

My immediate thought is no, of course not. I didn't kill Weston, so there's no way my prints would be on that knife. It would be Taylor's prints they'd find, whoever and wherever she was.

But that thought is quickly replaced by a more unsettling one. Why would Taylor have left the knife, if she'd planned this all along? Surely she wouldn't be that stupid.

On the other hand, if it was really me who'd killed Weston in a fit of a delusional rage, maybe I hadn't been sane enough to remember to take the knife with me. Isn't that what they call an unorganized killer? Maybe the prints *are* going to be a match to mine.

I fight off a wave of nausea. Minnie peers at me curiously. "Are you okay? You look like you've seen a ghost."

"No, I'm just — thinking how awful it must have been for Dina and Olga P."

"It was awful," she says. "I'm sure. Now, I'm sorry to cut this short. I really need to catch the train soon, otherwise I'll miss my bus."

We're already standing at the entry to the subway. Commuters push past us as they head down into the underground. Minnie tosses her cup and the rest of her tea into a nearby trashcan.

Before she disappears down the stairs, she turns to me. "If you did it, you should run."

"What?"

"I wouldn't blame you," Minnie insists. "That man got what was coming to him. But the police... I don't trust them. Never trust them. The stories I could tell you, things in my neighborhood, I've seen—"

"Minnie, I didn't kill him."

Her eyes narrow. "I'm saying that if you did, don't trust anything the police say to you. They're not on your side. They're never on your side."

"I didn't do it." Jesus. If even Minnie believes I killed him, what hope do I have of convincing anyone else that I'm not guilty? What hope do I even have of convincing myself?

Minnie reaches out and squeezes my hand, then lets go and disappears down the stairwell and into the subway.

———

I head home from there. I'd promised my mother that I wouldn't be late, and I have no business in the city, anyway. Not anymore. Manhattan is too fraught, too unpredictable. I long to be back in my own home, in my own bed.

By the time I get home, it's dark. Mom is in the kitchen, standing in front of the open fridge. The room feels cozy and warm, a haven against the night air.

"What do you want for dinner?" I ask, gently nudging her out of the way to inspect the contents of the fridge.

"I was thinking grilled cheese," she says. "I could make us some."

"Okay." *Curled cheese,* I think, remembering how I'd made Taylor laugh. But I try to smile. Mom knows it's one of my favorites from when I was a kid. "Do you want tomato soup with it?"

We tag team, Mom making the sandwiches and me on soup duty. When it's ready, we sit at the kitchen table to eat, instead of retreating to the living room and the numbing television game shows.

"I'm sorry that I haven't been your mother," Mom says. "When you needed me."

"Stop. What are you talking about?"

"I know that I'm not there for you. Not the way I want to be. Not the way you need me to be. After everything with your father, I—"

"It's okay, Mom. Really. We don't have to talk about it." I'm suddenly terrified that she's going to confess everything to me — what she did when pushed to the brink.

"Maybe that's the problem, Alice. We never talk about it."

"What's there to say? He was a bastard. He's gone. We're both better off. Whoever shot him did the right thing." I say it as emphatically as I dare.

"And look what it's done to both of us. He's gone, but I can't leave the house and you—"

"What about me?" All my goodwill has evaporated, and now, sitting there at that kitchen table, staring at my tomato soup, I'm nothing but empty and cold.

"Nothing, Alice. Just..." My mother sighs.

I've lost my appetite. I don't touch another bite of the soup or even the grilled cheese, and eventually, I clear the dishes away from the table. Mom goes into the living room but doesn't turn on the television. I wash the dishes by myself.

As I pass by the living room, I think about poking my head in. To apologize, maybe, or to at least say something to lighten the mood. But no words want to come out of my mouth. I start upstairs.

"Alice," my mother calls. "Could you do me a favor?"

"Sure."

"Can you get me the photo album? The old one with the burgundy leather cover. It's in the linen closet at the top of the stairs."

"Sure." I bound upstairs, happy to at least have a task to

do without complaint. Maybe that will make up for my earlier surliness.

In the linen closet, I locate the album behind a stack of Christmas tea towels that haven't seen the light of day in almost ten years. Not since before Dad died. I yank the album out and start back toward the stairs.

Before I can reach them, the doorbell rings. I freeze. We don't exactly get a lot of visitors. I peek out the window at the top of the stairs.

Shit.

A police cruiser is parked outside our house. I crane my neck to get a better view. Two men standing on our front stoop. I can't be totally sure from up here, but I'm pretty sure it's the same two from the other day. Detectives Douglas and Vyas.

Shit shit shit.

My legs have turned to lead, but I force myself back down the upstairs hallway. My bedroom is at the rear of the house, so it's the farthest from the front door, but it still offers little protection if they've come to arrest me.

Hold on. Maybe they're not here to arrest me. Maybe they just have a court order for my fingerprints.

But is that any better? I truly don't know what they're going to find on that knife. Most of me believes that I'm innocent, but there's enough of me that's still unconvinced that I don't dare give them the opportunity to find out for sure.

I creep back up into my bedroom and close the door lightly. Downstairs, Mom pads to the front door and unlocks the deadbolt. Another few seconds and they'll be in the house, and a minute after that they'll be calling for me to come downstairs.

I only have a split second to decide. That's probably a good thing, because any longer and I'd lose my nerve. I throw open my bedroom window and climb out onto the kitchen roof, already making for the getaway tree.

I have to get out of here.

I have to run.

TWENTY-SIX

ONCE I'M OUTSIDE, I don't think. I just run. Through the Archers' backyard, out onto Scribner Avenue, toward Westervelt. I run like I've never run before.

But when I reach Victory Boulevard, the reality of my situation sinks in. It's freezing cold and I'm out here with no jacket, just a thin t-shirt and jeans. I'm not even wearing shoes. My sock-covered feet are already turning numb against the cold concrete sidewalk.

I don't even have my phone to call for help — not that I know who I'd call. I've got my pocket knife and my wallet, though, so at least that's something. I'm down to about twenty dollars cash, but I've got my credit and debit cards. Will the police be able to track my credit card purchases? If I'd been able to grab my backpack, I'd have access to all that cash that I took out the other day, but I'd dropped it downstairs when I got home, and it's probably still sitting in the doorway, right where the cops had entered.

What am I doing? The true stupidity of my decision almost knocks me flat.

But I have to keep moving. The street is busy at this time of evening, and if the cops come looking for me, they'll almost certainly head this way. I can't be standing here when they do.

But where can I go? I can't head for the ferry. They'll think of that, and the twenty-five minutes I'm stuck on the harbor will give them ample time to put a welcoming committee in place for me on the other side.

But if I get an Uber or even a cab, they'll be able to track that, won't they? I'd have to use my credit card, which means they'll be able to find the driver and they'll figure out where I asked to be dropped off. But at the moment, that seems like my best option. My only option. I can keep moving once they drop me off. Figure this all out once I'm off the island and out of immediate danger.

I scan the oncoming traffic. In the distance, the rooftop light of a taxi glows, so I lift my arm in the air.

There's a squeal of brakes and the sound of several car horns honking at once. I stare in surprise at the car that's slammed to a stop right beside me. I almost bolt until I recognize the dark blue Camry.

Heath.

He rolls down the passenger side window and leans across. "Alice? What are you doing out here?"

"Go away."

I walk, trying to put some distance between us. The last thing I want to do is drag Heath down into this mess with me.

But instead of leaving, he inches the car forward slowly,

keeping pace with me. More people are leaning on their horns now, irritated that Heath hasn't sailed through the intersection already.

"Alice, come on. What are you doing? You're going to freeze to death out here."

"I'm fine, Heath. Don't worry about it."

"Alice, please. Talk to me."

Over the blare of car horns, something else catches my attention. In the distance, the slow wail of a police siren. *Shit.*

I only have a split second to decide, and even though I hate myself for doing it, I yank open the passenger side door of Heath's car and crawl in.

"You mind telling me what's going on? Jesus, Alice, are you not wearing shoes?"

"Just drive." I clench my jaw as I crane my neck to look behind us. No sign of the blue and red lights yet, but even from inside the car I can hear the sirens, which means they're getting closer.

The light in front of us turns from green to yellow, and I know we only have an instant to do this. "Go!"

He hits the gas and floors it through the intersection. The light turns red right behind us.

"Where to?" His shoulders are tense, and his eyes never leave the road.

Guilt consumes me. He's in this now. He's harboring a fugitive. Aiding and abetting a criminal. Or something. But I need him. If I don't tell him the truth, he can't be held accountable, right? He can say truthfully that he thought he was just giving his neighbor a ride. Surely, they wouldn't press any charges for that.

"I need to get into the city," I say. "I... was mugged."

"Shit, Alice, are you okay?"

"I'm fine. I just need to—" What? I don't even know what to do next. *Think, Alice. Think.*

Okay. I need time. Enough so that I can figure out how to fix this. How to find Taylor or gather enough proof that I had nothing to do with Weston's death. So I need a place to hide out in the meantime. I can't go home, and I can't go to Heath and Enid's house. I need a motel. Preferably a dodgy one where they don't check ID and are willing to turn a blind eye to the things their guests get up to.

But to stay at a motel, I need cash. I wish I'd been able to bring my backpack, but I guess you can't be choosy when you run from the police. Where are the Pinterest-pretty infographics for that, huh? *Evading Arrest: What to pack, what to skip, and the number one essential you don't want to be without!*

Once again, the reality of my situation hits me like a sledgehammer to the gut. I let myself close my eyes and rest my head against the upholstered seat of Heath's Camry.

When the car slows to a stop, I blink back to reality. We're at another traffic light. "I need to stop at an ATM."

"An ATM? I thought you were mugged."

"They didn't get my wallet. And I need cash."

"Come on, Alice, that can wait. You need to go to the police. Tell them what happened. Did they take your shoes? My God, I can't believe they'd take your shoes. Lowlifes." He swears, and I almost laugh. Almost.

"No one took my shoes." It's the most I'll give him for now. "I just need an ATM. And I need you to park far enough away from it that your car won't be caught on camera. If there are any. I don't want to take any chances."

Though I'm staring out at the road unspooling in front of us, I can feel the heat of Heath's gaze on me. "Alice, do you want to tell me what's going on? The truth, I mean."

"I will," I lie. "Just get me to an ATM first. I might need to hit a couple of them." If I do it now, if I collect the cash before the police can put a trace on my cards, it'll be better. And I have to get as much cash as I can. Within a few hours, I probably won't be able to use these cards again. All that cash sitting in my bank account will be completely useless to me.

Heath pulls to a stop in front of a 7-Eleven. "Will this do?"

"Perfect," I say. "Now stay here. Don't come inside."

I get out of the car and approach the store. I walk confidently when I enter, heading straight toward the back of the store where the machine is located. I pray no one notices that I'm not wearing shoes. *No shirt, no shoes, no service,* I chant to myself. But the cashier is busy with a couple of teenagers buying half a dozen Slurpees and enough burritos to feed a small army, and he pays almost no attention to me, other than a cursory nod when I walk in.

The machine has a thousand-dollar limit on it, so I enter the max and select withdraw. If I can hit three or four machines, that should be enough to last me for a little while. At least long enough to figure out where I'm going and what I'm going to do next.

I wait while the machine chugs through my request. It makes a whirring noise as two words flash on the screen.

'Insufficient funds.'

What? No. That's impossible. I eject my card and start the process over again. Maybe I accidentally hit the wrong account by mistake. I don't know if that's even possible, but it's more workable than the idea that five hundred grand just up and disappeared.

But I go through the process twice more, going through the menu carefully and punching in my PIN in slow motion, and each time, those same two words flare up on the screen.

'Insufficient funds.'

"No, no, no." I smack the side of the machine, earning a glare from the guy working behind the counter. I have to get out of here. I have to think.

I slink out of the store and, as I walk across the parking lot, I realize how badly my knees are shaking. By the time I get to Heath's car, I collapse into the passenger side.

"Are you going to tell me what's going on?"

"Not yet. I need to try another bank machine." Maybe the 'insufficient funds' message had nothing to do with my account. Maybe *the machine* had insufficient funds — after all, I'd asked for the full thousand. Maybe it didn't have enough cash left to dispense my request.

That has to be it. It has to be.

Heath says nothing but obliges my request. We stop at another convenience store a few blocks away, and once again I try to withdraw a thousand dollars. Once again, I'm denied.

I try a smaller withdrawal. Twenty dollars. That's gotta work.

Only it doesn't.

Back out to the car. All the blood feels like it's draining from my body. "Can we try another place?"

Heath wordlessly starts the car, and we try a third convenience store. This time I don't even have any hope. I test the machine just to be sure, but it once again displays the same message.

'Insufficient funds.'

A sob chokes me. I hurry back out to the car.

"You look like someone kicked you in the stomach," Heath says. He doesn't start the car.

"It's all gone."

"What's all gone?"

"Everything." I don't know how she did it, but Taylor had something to do with this.

My license — she had my license when she rented that apartment. What else did she have? I remember my wallet being stolen out of my locker at The Grant. Could that have been her? That means she could have everything — my debit card, my social security card. Would that have been enough for her to withdraw all of that money? She'd still need my PIN.

Then I remember the trip to the bank, on the first day I met her. How she'd stood beside me when I typed in my info at the teller's station.

The truth of it hits me all at once, like a punch to the stomach.

Taylor took my money. She set me up, and then she took everything.

TWENTY-SEVEN

SHE SURVEYED THE CROWD. *Looking for just the right couple. It would be perfect, or not at all.*

She walked through the shallow reflecting pool, flip-flops squishing with each step. A fine mist sprayed her as she navigated through the jets of water that shot up, and through the children that chased each other in and around them. After the sweltering heat of the day, she welcomed the coolness of the water. She wasn't the only one. Clinton Square was crowded with bodies, all hot and tired from a long day of shopping or sightseeing or whatever the hell else people came here to do. Music played somewhere; the atmosphere was convivial. Couples in sunglasses licked ice cream cones, parents with sunburned cheeks handed out ice-cold cans of cola to excited children.

It had been easy enough to get here. It was surprising how many people were willing to pick up a solo hitchhiker, especially a young woman. It had taken her only three hours to get to Syracuse.

No one knew she was here. Shannon and Jim never asked any questions when she left the house, or at least they didn't ask enough, or the right ones. They thought she was with Caitlin, studying for their history final. They were too nice for their own good, really, and if you were too nice, you eventually crossed all the way into idiot territory.

There were lots of idiots here, too. She could feel it. She could see it in the set of their shoulders, in the easy way they left their bags at their feet.

She crisscrossed the pool a couple of times, her eyes peeled for the ones. She never came with any preconceived ideas of what she was looking for, but she always knew it when she saw it. It would hit her like a twisting of the gut.

But today, there was no one. She wasn't getting the vibe. The sun would set soon, and it would do no good to search after dark. People got more cautious once that happened. Either that, or they got too drunk. Neither was great.

She had almost given up when she spotted them. A middle-aged couple, maybe a few years older than Shannon and Jim. The wife had auburn hair that hung straight down over her shoulders; the husband had darker hair, an olive complexion. He wore sunglasses, but even underneath she could tell that his face was handsome. Chiseled. The sunglasses were expensive, she noted. The wife wore a pair of Jimmy Choo sandals.

She looked away, but crossed the fountain until she was next to them. She perched on the edge of the fountain, gazing distractedly at her phone. She listened to them for a few minutes.

"We can try again if you want to, honey," the man was

saying. "I just don't see the point. We've tried three times. Where do we draw the line?" His words were angry, but his voice sounded tired.

"We draw the line when we're holding our baby," the woman said, through tears.

Oh, this was even better than Sam could have hoped. She kept scrolling through her phone, hoping it looked as if she was lost in her own world.

"And if it doesn't work?" the man said to his wife. "Are you going to be able to handle that?"

She shook her head. "I don't know. But I know I can't handle this, either. I feel like a piece of me is missing, Scott. I feel like I've lost an arm or something."

"I know, honey. I know."

Sam could hear the defeat in his voice, his desire to give his wife anything she wanted. She had to bite back the cackle that threatened to escape her lips.

She readied herself. Bit the inside of her cheek so that her eyes would water.

"Excuse me," she said, her voice wavering. "Do you know how to get to the bus station from here?"

The man looked surprised, as if he hadn't noticed her sitting there. It would be the last moment of his life where he wouldn't know her. She'd haunt his thoughts for years to come. "Yeah, it's about a five-minute drive from here."

"Oh." She tried to look worried. "How long would it take to walk?"

He looked at his wife. "I don't know. Maybe forty-five minutes?"

"An hour," she amended.

"Oh no." Sam let the tears flow. "I'm totally going to miss my bus."

She felt the couple beside her exchange a look.

"Do you need a ride?" the guy, Scott, asked.

"I don't want to bother you," she said. "It's my own stupid fault, anyway."

"Oh, come on," the woman said. "It's no problem. Honestly. Let us drive you."

"Are you sure?"

"Absolutely." The woman was already standing, hitching her purse — Louis Vuitton — over her shoulder. "Let's go."

"Thank you so much. My name's Lisa, by the way."

Sam followed them to their car. While they walked, she gave them her sob story — a foster kid in the city for a high school debate meet. She'd skipped the ride home with her classmates because she wanted to buy a present for her foster mother — a piece by a local artist. Only the art gallery had been closed when she got there, and now she was about to miss the last bus home.

She could feel them eating up every morsel she dropped. Now they weren't just Good Samaritans helping out a kid, they were virtuous saviors, coming to the aid of an underprivileged foster kid. God, people lapped that shit up.

When they pulled up in front of the bus station a few minutes later, Sam smiled. "Thank you so much," she said again. "I really appreciate it."

"You got your ticket?" The woman — who had introduced herself as Mel — asked.

"I do." Sam pulled it out of her pocket and held it out. "See? Three p.m., September 21, Syracuse to Buffalo."

"Twenty-first?" Mel wrinkled her nose. "Honey, it's the twentieth today."

"Oh no. Are you sure?" Sam pretended to peer at the ticket, even though she knew exactly what it said. "Oh my God. I'm such a dummy." This time, she turned on the full waterworks.

Scott looked uncomfortable, but Mel was leaning into the back seat, her hand on Sam's knee. "Hey. Don't worry about it. Maybe you can change it."

"Okay." She sniffled. "You're right. I'll go in and see. Hopefully it'll be no big deal."

"I'll come with you," Mel said. "Honey, wait here."

Scott sighed, but said nothing.

Sam and Mel exited the car and walked together into the bus station. Sam didn't worry when Mel came up to the counter with her. She'd already checked the bus schedule and had specifically timed it so that there wasn't another bus to Buffalo until tomorrow. But when the old guy working at the ticket counter informed her of this, she made sure to lose it.

"I'm so stupid," she wailed to Mel. "My foster mom is going to kill me."

"Do you think she could come get you?"

Sam wiped her eyes. "Maybe. I don't know. My foster dad is on a business trip, and my mom is home alone with all the other kids. The twins are only nine months, and they both had fevers this morning. I feel so bad making her drive all the way up here to get me." She unleashed another sob.

Mel put an arm around her. "Don't cry, sweetie. You're going to be okay. You can stay with us tonight. How about that? We'll call your mom from our place and let her know you're okay."

"Are you sure?" Sam asked between sniffles. "What about Scott?"

"Oh, don't you worry about him. We'd both be happy to have you."

"Okay." She offered a perfectly practiced wobbly-but-grateful smile. "I really appreciate it."

As predicted, Scott wasn't terribly pleased about the whole thing, but he put on a smile for Mel's sake. They drove back to Scott and Mel's place. As soon as they pulled up to the three-car garage, Sam knew she'd made an excellent choice this time. They were loaded. The house sprawled over a neatly landscaped lot, and Sam tried to keep her mouth from hanging open as she followed them in through the garage.

Mel called Sam's foster mother, as promised, and got her voicemail. Which was, of course, a Google Voice number that Sam had set up, just for such occasions. Mel left a message, saying that 'Lisa' was staying with them, and if she had any concerns, she could call anytime. Sam knew there'd be no call.

Mel showed her to a guest bedroom, complete with its own en suite, and left her to shower and change. Sam took her time, showering quickly, and creeping around the rest of the second floor to scope the place out. This would do. This would do quite nicely, indeed.

By the time Mel and Scott drove her back to the bus station the next day, Sam's bag was loaded down with a three-hundred-dollar bottle of scotch, a couple of hundred bucks from Scott's wallet, a MacBook Air that she'd found stuffed in a magazine rack, and a necklace from the bottom of Mel's *jewelry box, a white gold turtle with an emerald stone for a shell. Given how tricked out their house was, she doubted they'd discover any of the losses for at least a few days, and by then, she'd have disappeared. If they looked for her at all, they'd be looking for Lisa in Buffalo, not Sam in Ithaca. And she doubted they'd even look that far — most people were far too embarrassed to admit they got conned to actually dwell on finding the person who'd conned them. No, she imagined Mel and Scott would try to put the whole thing behind them as soon as possible.*

She would do the same. It didn't matter what she stole, or what she walked away with — in the end it felt as if there was always more to do. Always another sucker to befriend.

TWENTY-EIGHT

"JESUS, Alice. Are you okay? Do you need a hospital?" Heath leans over me, concerned.

I realize I just moaned out loud. I sit up straight in my seat. "I'm fine. I need—" God. What do I even need? A time machine so I can go back and never swivel my bar stool toward Taylor that first day at El Diablo? "Money. I'm so sorry, Heath. But do you have any cash I can borrow? I swear I'll pay you back as soon as I can. Sooner."

"Is that all? Of course, you can borrow money. Come on."

We go back into the convenience store and huddle in front of the machine.

"How much do you need?" he asks.

"I don't know. As much as you can spare."

He studies the screen in front of him. "Well, the max is two thousand. Is that enough? If not, we can go to another machine."

"Two is enough." I want to weep with gratitude. "Are you sure you can afford it?"

"I've been saving up." He shrugs. "Hoping to buy an apartment at some point."

I want to cry again, but this time out of guilt. "I swear I'll pay you back. Every penny. With interest."

Heath withdraws the cash, and I stuff it into my wallet. As we make our way out of the store, a row of feminine products catches my eye. Maybe they also have...

I duck down that aisle and spot what I'm looking for. I choose a box marked 'Dark Chestnut,' boasting a picture of a smiling woman with glossy brown hair. I zip quickly around the store, hoping that maybe they'll have some cheap plastic shower sandals or even flip-flops, but no dice. I pay for the hair dye and take my plastic bag with me out of the store. If Heath finds this to be a strange purchase, he doesn't say so.

As we cross the convenience store parking lot toward the car, sirens wail in the distance. I freeze.

Heath takes two more steps before realizing I'm not behind him. "What? Why'd you stop?"

"Do you hear that?"

"What?"

"Sirens."

"Yeah."

I take a deep breath. "We have to go. *Now*."

Despite the approaching cop cars, Heath and I take our time strolling toward the Camry. Better to not look suspicious. I mark every step, counting down as I close the distance between the store and the relative safety of the car. The sirens get louder until, when we're almost at the car, two police cruisers sail into view.

This is it. They're going to see me and pull over and

arrest me, and now I can add evading arrest and maybe obstruction of justice to the murder charge.

But as I watch, the cruisers continue on past the convenience store. They don't stop, don't slow. Just fly on by until they're out of sight and the sound of the sirens dies away. I sprint the rest of the way to the car and slip into the passenger side. I sink low in the seat, so my face is barely visible through the window.

"Alice. Seriously," Heath says as he slides into the driver's side. "What the hell is going on?"

"I need to get off this island. Now. Can you take me into the city?"

"I thought you wanted to go to the police."

"I do. I mean, I will. But I need to find a place to stay first. I need a hotel. No, a motel. Do you know anything? Something kind of shady. Where I can hide out for a bit."

"Why do you have to hide out? Who are you hiding from?"

"It's better if you don't know."

"I'll be the judge of that."

"Please, Heath. I'm trying to protect you."

"I don't need protecting."

"From this, you do." From *me*, you do.

I think he's going to argue the point, but to my surprise and relief, he pulls out of the parking lot of the convenience store.

We drive in silence for a while. His anger mixes with curiosity and bubbles between us, but he doesn't push, and for that I'm grateful.

When we're off the island, I breathe easier. Not a lot, but at least a little.

"Do you have a motel in mind?" he grunts at one point.

"No," I admit. "Do you know anything like that? Somewhere I could... hide out for a bit?"

He huffs. "There's the Sunset Motel. They rent by the hour so they have a lot of, um, working girls there. It's not exactly the safest place in the world, but I don't think they'd ask any questions."

"You're sure?" What I really want to ask is 'how would you know that?'

"I'm sure. My buddy at work goes there once in a while. To, uh, patronize a woman who works there." He flushes. "Nasty divorce. He calls it stress relief."

A small and stupid part of me is relieved to hear that.

"It sounds perfect." My definition of perfect has changed a great deal in the last twenty-four hours.

Heath takes me to the motel, a two-story number that was once painted a pale blue but is now a dingy sort of non-color, like old dried cement. The neon sign jutting up out of the parking lot features neon palm trees, an obscene contrast to the grey pavement that surrounds the complex.

"Thanks for the ride," I say, already opening the door. "If you wouldn't mind not telling anyone you saw me..."

"I'm coming in with you," he announces before I can finish.

"No, you're not."

"I am. I'm not leaving you here by yourself. Do you know what kind of people come here?"

"I'm not worried about a few sex workers. I'm sure they don't give a shit about me." That, at least, is the truth.

"Neither am I. But I'm worried about their clients, about their dealers and their bosses. I don't like you being here alone. This was a bad idea."

"This is my only option right now."

"Alice, talk to me. Tell me what's going on."

Instead of answering, I get out of the car and head toward the door marked 'Office.' Flecks of peeling yellow paint flake off as soon as I grab the handle. I step inside; Heath is right behind me.

"I need a room," I tell the man behind the counter. He's got a shaved head, but his skull is too small and his face too pinched to pull it off. Instead of giving the appearance of toughness, it makes him look like a peeled grape.

"Twenty an hour. Seventy for a whole night."

"Um. A week. For now."

"By the week, it's four fifty even."

I breathe in relief. You can't get a room at The Grant for one night for that price. I grab my wallet and thrust the cash at him.

"ID?" he asks, counting the bills and not looking at me.

"I, uh—" I glance at Heath, who shrugs. "I don't have any. I lost my wallet."

He peers up, his eyes flicking to my wallet, which is clearly in my hands. "No problem. That'll be an extra three hundred."

"For what?"

"For my discretion," he says, with a sour smile.

I can't afford to argue, so I slap another three hundred

dollars down on the counter. In exchange, he slides over two silver keys, each attached to a plastic palm tree. One to me and one to Heath. I don't have time to decide how I feel about that.

"Room two fourteen. Second floor, around back near the ice machine."

"Thanks."

Heath walks me all the way to the room. His disapproval vibrates off him the entire way, and when I unlock the door to the room, he groans.

"Alice, really. There has to be a better option. I can help you."

"You can't help me, Heath. No one can help me."

We step inside the room, letting the door swing closed behind us. I scope the place out. It's honestly not as bad as I expected. The walls are a pale blue, and a picture of the beach hangs over the bed. The bed is a double, with a thin bedspread in variegated yellows and browns. I wonder if someone chose it because it looked a bit like beach sand, or if it was because the mottled colors would do a bang-up job of masking stains. I decide I'd prefer not to know the answer to that. There's a window next to the door, with pale green curtains, and, on either side of it, a guest chair. Opposite the bed is a stand with a few drawers. On top of that sits a small flat screen television, chained to the stand. There's a bathroom at the far end of the room.

"Thank you for getting me here," I say to Heath, hoping he'll take the hint and go.

Instead, he perches on the edge of the bed. "I'm not leaving."

"You have to."

"Are you going to make me?"

I stare at him. I want to say yes, but when I take in his sturdy frame, his crossed arms, I know there's no way I could physically force him to leave if he doesn't want to. The best I can do is make it so that the choice is his.

"Fine. You want to know what's going on? Did you hear about that guy who was killed at The Grant? Weston Chambers?"

His brow wrinkles in confusion. "I heard about it. What does that have to do with anything?"

"The police want to arrest me for his murder."

Shock registers on his face. "What? Why the hell would they do that?"

I take a deep breath. "Because I think I might have done it."

TWENTY-NINE

HEATH STARES at me in utter shock. It would almost be comical if it wasn't so deadly serious.

"So, you see," I conclude. "You're helping a wanted criminal. And the longer you stick around, the more culpable you are. You need to leave. Go home and forget you ever saw me."

He's quiet for a minute. I think I might have broken his brain, which again is almost funny, except that it's not.

When he speaks, there's a steely determination in his voice. "I'm sorry, Alice, but no way did you kill that guy. I don't believe it, and I have no idea why you'd say you did. Secondly, I'm not leaving you on your own. You don't even have shoes, for God's sake."

I look down at my feet. The bottoms of the white sports socks have turned black with the filth of three convenience stores and the motel parking lot. The manic laughter that's been threatening to erupt finally spills over, and I sputter out a giggle. Another bursts out, and I collapse backward onto the bed, laughing so hard that tears roll down my cheeks.

"What's so funny?" Heath asks tentatively. "This is a joke, right? This whole thing is, what, some kind of setup?"

"I... don't... have... any shoes," I pant, still howling with laughter. "I ran from the cops and I wasn't even wearing shoes. Who does that?" I dissolve into another gale of laughter, but Heath doesn't join me.

"What do you need?"

I don't answer. I can't; I'm still laughing too hard.

"Alice." Heath grabs my shoulders and shakes them.

Staring into his grey eyes, his face so close to mine, my laughter evaporates. The weight of a thousand worlds settles in on my shoulders. I hiccup once.

Heath's breath is warm on my face. "Pull yourself together and talk to me."

"Go home," I tell him. "I appreciate your faith in me, and your desire to help. I really do. But the police are probably going to go to your house to talk to Enid. I need you to make sure she's okay. And my mom—" My voice catches. My poor mother. "Check on my mother. Please, Heath."

His jaw tightens. "Fine. That, I'll do. But I'll be back in the morning. I'll bring you shoes. Some clothes. Food. You can't stay in here all week without supplies. You need help."

I don't want to admit it, but he's right. Even with the hair dye, I'm not sure I have the courage to leave the motel room, and I definitely can't keep running around with no shoes. And the fact is, I don't have the energy to continue arguing with him.

"Fine," I sigh. "Come back tomorrow."

"We'll figure this out, Alice," he says. "I promise."

I don't believe him, but I try to smile. I appreciate his confidence, even though it's completely misplaced.

After I finally usher Heath out the door of my motel room, I collapse backward onto the bed. Now that the adrenaline is wearing off, dread is filling in the grooves.

I'm on the run, but I have no plan. I was afraid to face the police, but how else is this going to end? Do I go into hiding for the rest of my life?

The only option is to find Taylor, but I have no idea where to look.

So what else can I do? Maybe I could find some proof that she was the one who did this. But what? I don't have my phone, but I try to remember the text messages we exchanged. I know she never mentioned the murder in her messages, but did I ever say anything to her about *not* doing it? That might count for something. But as hard as I try to recall, I don't think I ever did. I'm pretty sure the only times we talked about it were over the phone or in person.

No other answers come to me, so I decide to focus instead on something practical. I grab the hair dye, purchased from the last convenience store, and head to the bathroom.

Forty minutes later, I've stained my mousy blonde hair a dark chestnut brown. The contrast of the dark locks against my pale skin is eye-catching, but I still see too much of myself in the mirror. I grab my knife from the pocket of my jeans, which I'd tossed on the bed along with my t-shirt as soon as I busted open the hair dye. I take the knife into the bathroom and flick it open.

I hack off a section of my hair, and then another and

another. I do it as neatly as I can, but it still looks like I gave myself a haircut with a dull knife, which is, in fact, exactly what I did. But once my hair is up around my chin, the shorter length combined with the darker color is enough to satisfy me that I look suitably different.

I study my reflection in the mirror for a long time. At my familiar brown eyes, at my pale lips, at the faint dusting of freckles that lope over my nose and trail off across the apples of my cheeks. The features are so familiar, and yet it's like looking into the face of a stranger. It's not just the hair, either. It's the unknowing.

Did I kill Weston Chambers? Could I have done it?

I go to bed, uneasy and wired but also dead tired. I don't think I'll sleep, but to my surprise, I'm gone in minutes.

In the morning, I'm awoken by pounding on my motel door.

I jump out of bed, panic and adrenaline coursing through me. They're here. They've found me. How could I have let myself relax like that?

I yank on my jeans and t-shirt and peer through the peephole in the door. I breathe a sigh of relief. It's only Heath.

I look both ways on the second-floor deck before I pull him into the room with me and slam the door closed behind him. He's laden down with stuff — two plastic shopping bags are slung over one arm, and in the other he carries a paper bag stained with grease and a tray with two to-go coffee cups on it.

Even though I'd been determined to do this on my own, seeing Heath here in my room fills me with enormous and unspeakable relief. And not just because of the coffee, though I eye those cups like I'm an apex predator.

"This is yours." He nudges the one in the corner toward me. "It's black, the way you like it. And I brought breakfast sandwiches."

I almost want to cry, but I'm too busy slurping down the coffee. "Thank you," I manage, after I've sucked back a third of it. I'm already digging into the paper bag, pulling out a breakfast sandwich so greasy it's rendered the waxy paper surrounding it transparent. I take a huge bite. I didn't realize how hungry I was.

When I finally feel halfway normal again, I look up to find Heath staring at me. No, not at me. At my hair. I touch the short locks self-consciously. "I know. It's weird."

"No, I like it. It looks nice."

"Thanks." The silence between us takes on a different color, a distinct flavor. I look away as I inhale the last half of my sandwich just to distract myself, and wipe my hands on my jeans.

"What's in the bags?"

"Oh." He recovers. "Some clothes. I got them from Enid. You guys are about the same size, I think."

"We are." I don't mention that Enid and I have completely opposite styles. But I guess maybe that's the point. I don't want to look like myself.

I root through the bags, unearthing a couple of sweaters, two t-shirts, and a pair of sneakers. There's also a pair of jeans. *Pink* jeans.

Heath shrugs when I hold them up. "I didn't have a lot of options, okay? I tried to grab stuff she wouldn't notice."

"So you didn't tell her anything about this?"

He looks away, guilty.

"Heath."

"I didn't tell her where you were. But the police came to our house last night. Enid was really upset. So I told her you were fine. That you were safe. I had to put her mind at ease."

I want to be mad at him, but after everything he's already done for me, I can't bring myself all the way there. And I wouldn't want Enid to worry, anyway. "As long as she doesn't say anything."

"She won't. She'd never. Enid would probably die before she let anything happen to you. She worships you, you know."

Great. Back to feeling uncomfortable. I grab the pink jeans, a t-shirt, and a cardigan and take them into the bathroom. "Thanks for all this stuff. I'm going to have a shower. You can show yourself out."

I close the bathroom door before he can reply. The shower sputters to life and I climb in, losing myself for a couple of minutes under the hot, pelting stream. Okay, pelting is a stretch. It's more of a slow dribble, but it's enough to wash away the sleep and some of the battery tang of adrenaline, and when I step out, I'm at least slightly refreshed.

I pull on the pink jeans and inspect the t-shirt. It's burgundy and features a cartoon cup of tea. The text says: *Chai Harder*. Great. Totally inconspicuous. I pull the yellow cardigan over it. I feel ridiculous, but I have to admit, as I ponder my reflection in the steamy mirror, that I look nothing like Alice Brewster.

When I emerge from the bathroom, steam trails after me.

"That's... different," a voice says from the corner of the room.

I jump. "Heath. I thought you were leaving."

"I never said that."

"No, but I did."

He shrugs. "Do the clothes fit okay?"

"They're fine." I tug at the sleeve of the cardigan. It's way more form-fitting than the clothes I normally wear, which lean toward big, baggy, and masculine.

"I wish Enid could see you now. She'd love this."

At that, I crack a smile. She would. Her favorite activity when we were in high school was 'Alice Gets A Makeover,' in which I'd let her dress me up and put makeup on me, like I was a life-sized doll or a chick from a bad nineties teen movie. I didn't do it very often, but it always made her immeasurably happy when I did. "There," she'd announce, with a final flourish of lipstick. "Now you're just perfect."

"Tell her she has to stop buying t-shirts with cartoon food on them. She's twenty-five years old, for God's sake."

Heath chuckles. "I'll pass along the message. Now, what's next?"

"What do you mean, what's next?"

"I mean, what's next? What's the plan?" He hesitates, frowning. "There *is* a plan, right?"

I sit down on the bed and grab my coffee cup off the nightstand where I'd left it before my shower. There's still a third of a cup in there, and like hell am I going to waste it. "Not as such, no."

Heath groans. "Malice, you're killing me here. Sorry — pun not intended."

"I didn't have a lot of time to think this through, okay? The police showed up at my house and I panicked. I ran."

"Well..." He sits back in the chair. "What do you want to do? Do you want to keep running? You want to, what, start over? New life?"

"No. I don't know." Besides the fact that I have no idea how I'd do that, the thought of leaving my mother rips me apart inside. I don't know how she'd cope without me, and I don't know how I could do that to her.

Besides, running feels like giving up. I gave up when I accepted that check and let The Grant silence me. If I give up now, who am I?

But I don't know what to do next. The opposite of running is fighting, but I don't even know who or what I'm fighting.

Heath must read the confusion on my face, because he leans in. "Look, let's take a step back. Why don't you tell me what's happening? Why would you think you killed this Chambers guy?"

I gaze up at Heath's kind face, at the concern in his eyes. I decide to do something I should have done ages ago. I tell the truth.

THIRTY

AS I TALK, a myriad of expressions play out over Heath's face. Disbelief, anger, shock, sorrow, and maybe even something that looks like rueful admiration.

"Let me get this straight," he says when I finish speaking. "It was her idea to kill this guy. You tried to stop her. She got a job at The Grant—"

"She *might* have gotten a job at The Grant. I couldn't confirm that."

"Okay, she might have gotten a job there. And then she just... killed this guy. But why would she think you wanted that? Why would the police automatically think you did it?"

Okay, when I said I told Heath everything, I may have left out one tiny detail. I've said nothing to him about the rape. *The thing* that put all of this in motion. I've let him believe that Weston Chambers was just a regular entitled asshole who liked to piss off the cleaning staff. I can't stand to think of the way he'd look at me if he knew the real story, like

I was a fragile little bird that was dumb enough to fall from the nest.

"Because we had a bit of a run-in before I left The Grant," is all I tell him. "It was sort of what led to me losing my job there. The police think that's motive."

Heath shakes his head. "That's weak, Alice. It's certainly not enough to make me think you had anything to do with this."

"Thanks. But there's something weird here. I can't find any trace of Taylor now. Nothing adds up. It's like she didn't exist at all. It's like... it's like I made her up," I whisper.

"I don't believe that. You're not crazy, Alice. But let's take this one step at a time." He paces from one end of the room to the other, which takes all of about three steps with his long stride. "How can we prove you didn't do it? Where were you when he was killed?"

"They asked me about that. But I was in Central Park by myself. Waiting for Taylor, actually. She was supposed to meet me there. We were going to have a picnic."

"And let me guess — she never showed."

"Right. So I have no alibi. I can't prove I was in the park. I can't even prove she asked me to meet her there. We talked about it over the phone, so there are no text messages."

He growls something unintelligible.

"I know," I lament. "That's why I'm screwed. And what if I just... made it all up? What if I really killed him and I invented all this pretense around Taylor?" Finally voicing my fears clarifies something inside me, like thick butter turning to clear ghee.

But Heath only rolls his eyes. "Come on, Alice. You can't really believe that."

When I don't answer, he stops in front of me. Puts his hands on the bed, one on either side of me. Leans in close. "Alice Brewster, you listen to me. You didn't kill this guy. No way, no how. This Taylor person set you up. I don't know why or to what end, but it's clear as day to me. You didn't do this; she did."

I breathe out a sigh of relief. Hearing Heath say that is a salve to my soul. To my great horror, a tear rolls down my cheek. I huff out a laugh, but before I can swipe it away, Heath is using his knuckle to wipe it from my skin. I let out another shaky breath and duck out from under him.

"So if I didn't do it, what do I do now?"

"I think we have to find Taylor. If we can figure out why she did this, maybe we can figure out a way to prove your innocence. That you were framed."

It doesn't escape my attention that every time I use the word 'I,' Heath responds with 'we.' As much as I hate myself for letting him become embroiled in this, I'm grateful that he's here.

"But I don't know how we're going to find her," I admit. "I've tried everything. Her phone is disconnected, and the apartment she was living in was a dead end. She even lied about her roommate and her ex-boyfriend."

"Was there anything else she told you? Anything at all?"

"She said she was an actress. And that's about the only thing I believe. She certainly has a talent for it."

"Did she mention having auditions? Roles that she talked

about? If she was in a play, or a commercial, maybe we could track her that way."

I shake my head. "Not that I can think of. Just vague stuff."

"Is it worth looking her up on IMDB? Would she be on there?"

"Maybe. I know she was auditioning for some commercials. She might have done some short films. But I don't know her last name."

"Let's see how many Taylors there are."

He pulls out his phone, types a few things into the Internet Movie Database, and frowns. "Not as many as I expected, actually. Maybe you can spot her."

I take the phone and hold my breath as I scroll. He's right — there aren't that many Taylors. But none of the ones that appear are my Taylor. "She's not here."

"What if we try googling her?" he suggests. "Even if you don't know her last name, maybe we could turn something up. 'Taylor, New York, actress,' that kind of thing."

"Maybe," I say, hope rising in me. But when I try it, the results are overwhelming. The details are too vague, too common. Millions of results turn up; there's no way I can ever go through all of them.

"What about her life besides being an actress? She must have had a regular job," Heath says. "She was able to rent that Airbnb for a month, so she's got to have cash."

"Right." I lean forward. "She said she worked at a coffee shop. I never asked the name of it."

Heath frowns. "That's about as generic as being an actress. Did she at least mention the neighborhood?"

I shake my head. "She once said that it was crowded with students in the afternoon," I say, thinking back to the time I'd offered to come visit her. But was that the truth, or an excuse for why I couldn't go?

"What kind of students?" Heath asks. He's scrolling through his phone again. "If it's college students, that narrows it down a bit."

"She didn't specify. It could have been college students, high school kids, middle school — I have no idea."

Heath sighs. I feel like an idiot now that I realize how very little I really know about Taylor. She was a virtual stranger to me, and yet I let her into my life. No, worse than that — I practically begged her to come on in. It makes me sick to think of the hopeful way I'd waited for her text messages, of the thrill I'd felt when she'd called me sour, bright, and classic.

"Frosting Queen," I say with a jolt.

"Sorry?"

"Frosting Queen. It's a cupcake place. She said she used to work there."

"Do you think it was another lie?"

"I don't know. Maybe. But it sort of slipped out, like she hadn't really meant to say it. There's a chance it could have been the truth."

"Frosting Queen," Heath recites, tapping on his phone. "It's local. There are only two locations. Did she say which one she worked at?"

"No."

"Doesn't matter; we can hit both of them."

I hesitate. I fully intend to go to Frosting Queen, but I

still feel guilty for dragging Heath into my mess. "Don't you have to work today?"

"I already fixed that."

"Fixed it how?" Him calling in sick might raise some red flags, if anyone checks.

"Don't worry about it. You know my buddy going through the nasty divorce? Let's just say he owes me big time. I don't know how many times I had to cover for him when shit was going down with his wife."

"Are you sure?"

"I'm sure. He can handle a couple of days' worth of calls on his own. No one at the head office knows I'm not there, and Tony's not going to say anything. No one'll even notice I'm gone."

Heath works as an electrician, I know, but I have no idea what his day-to-day schedule is like. I have no choice but to trust him on that. I still feel guilty, though. "You've already done so much for me."

"What's your point?" He stands. "You ready?"

But I'm already standing, bundling myself into the mint green peacoat Heath had brought from Enid's closet. I ignore the fact that I look like an Easter egg and grab the palm tree key to my hotel room. "Let's go."

THIRTY-ONE

THERE'S no point trying to find parking downtown, so Heath parks his car in a commuter parking lot and we take the train into Manhattan. Once we're there, it doesn't take long to find Frosting Queen. The awning is bright pink, and the logo blares a bright picture of a pink-frosted cupcake wearing a glittering crown.

Heath pulls open the front door — also pink — and we step inside. I'm immediately blasted with the smell of vanilla and warm sugar. A glass counter glows with a display of over two dozen varieties of cupcake, each more elaborate than the last.

"Welcome to Frosting Queen," the girl behind the counter greets us, her voice high and breathy. She's got curly blonde hair, dimples as big as teaspoons, and she's wearing, aptly, a silver tiara and a pale blue ballgown. Her name tag says Queen Cheryl. She curtsies as we approach the counter. "What's your pleasure?"

"Actually, we're trying to track down someone who used to work here," I tell her.

Immediately, she straightens her curtsy. Her singsong voice drops an octave or two. "Sure. What was her name?"

"Taylor. I don't know her last name."

"Hm. I can't recall anyone with that name, but I've only worked here a year. How long ago did she work here?"

"I'm not sure."

"And you're sure she worked at this location? We have another one near Times Square."

"I'm really not sure. All I know is she used to work here."

She frowns at me. "I don't think I can help you."

"Really? Don't you keep, like, records of employees?"

She purses her lips. "Of course we do. Though I can't say we're in the habit of giving them out to total strangers."

"Is there a manager or something we could talk to?"

"The stores are owned by Lola Hardwick. She's working out of the other location today. She might agree to help you. No promises, though. She's not exactly..." Queen Cheryl trails off, her lips twisting in a grim smile. "Well, you'll see."

We grab a cab over to the second location of Frosting Queen. This one is even bigger, and far busier. It's clearly the original location and probably where we should have started. There are three young women working behind the counter, all wearing ballgowns and tiaras, all chirping in high voices, like cartoon mice.

We stand in line behind a family of six, waiting

impatiently as the children take forever to pick out two cupcakes apiece.

When we finally get to move up to the register, the clearly exhausted girl behind the counter — Queen Melody, according to her name tag — plasters on a huge artificial smile. "Welcome to Frosting Queen, what's your pleasure?"

"Actually, we're looking for Lola Hardwick. We were told she was here today."

"She's in the back. Is she expecting you?"

"No, but this is important. We really have to speak to her. About a former staff member."

"I'll see if she has time to meet with you."

Queen Melody disappears through a swinging door I hadn't even noticed — it's painted in the same pale pink and white stripes as the wall. As we wait, a line begins to form behind us. The other two queens behind the counter do their best to keep up, but as the shop gets more crowded, my anxiety creeps up. Even with my new hair and bizarrely pastel wardrobe, I'm terrified that the police are going to bust down the door at any moment.

Finally, Melody emerges from the back room. "You can go in. She has a couple of minutes."

Heath and I push through the door. I'm expecting more of the same teeth-achingly sweet decor — the pink walls, the crystal chandeliers, the white marble tiles veined in gold — but this area looks like the back of any restaurant. The walls are painted primer-white and lined with metal shelving units that store huge bags of sugar, sacks of flour, stacks of mixing bowls.

"All the way through, last door on the right," Queen Melody calls before letting the door swing closed behind us.

We pass a huge kitchen where three hustling bakers ignore us completely, then find the door to the office and knock before entering.

Lola Hardwick sits behind a large metal desk, a remnant from the seventies with faux wood paneling on the sides. Instead of being blonde, bubbly, and wearing a crown like her employees, she's got short hair, a pixie cut that's been dyed black. She wears a tight black t-shirt, showing off sleeve tattoos that snake up both arms. More abstract designs peek out above her collarbone, and scripted letters run up the tendon of her neck, stopping just below her jaw.

I can't say that I ever imagined the true Frosting Queen would have a neck tattoo.

"Melody says you're looking for someone," she says. She barely looks up from the beat-up laptop in front of her.

"Yes." I step forward. "Her name is Taylor. She's... an old friend from college. We lost touch, and I'm trying to find her."

"What's her last name?"

"Um... I don't know."

"Must have been a really good friend."

I don't reply. Lola taps a few keys on her keyboard. I wonder if she's actually looking at her personnel files or if she's playing spider solitaire.

"I'm not sure when she worked here," I offer.

"She didn't."

"Are you sure? She told me she—"

"I'm sure. I've hired every single person who's ever

worked here, and I can tell you right off the top of my head that we've never employed anyone named Taylor. Is it possible she worked here as a contractor with another vendor? Yes, it's possible. We have a cleaning company that manages both locations. We have suppliers who send regular deliveries, and some of them have had the same drivers for years. I have no idea off the top of my head if any of them are named Taylor, though. You'd have to contact those companies directly. But if your friend Taylor said she worked here, as in here in the shop, she didn't. I guarantee it."

Lola's tone brooks no argument. Neither does her neck tattoo. I look up at Heath, and he shrugs. There's nothing else for us to do here. Just another dead end.

Just another lie.

"Thanks for your time," I say. I can't keep the resentment out of my voice.

For the first time, Lola looks up. She peers over at me, her brow wrinkling. "You look familiar," she says. "Do we know each other?"

Something in her tone sends a frisson of fear through me. "I don't think so."

"Did you go to NYU?"

"No."

"No..." She taps her lip. "Ever do roller derby?"

"No."

"We should get going, *Katie*," Heath says, taking my arm and leading me from the room. He gives me a pointed look.

"Do you live in Chelsea?" Lola asks. "Maybe I know you from the neighborhood. The dog park?"

"No." Heath is really pulling on me now, so forcefully

that I have no choice but to follow him. "Thanks again for your help."

"It's going to come to me," Lola says, still studying me.

But by then, Heath and I are back in the hallway. He rushes me past the metal shelving units and back into the main part of the store, which is quieter than when we left.

"Did you get everything you needed?" Melody chirps.

"Yes, thanks." Heath ushers me outside and onto the street.

"What was that about?" I ask. "And who's Katie?"

"What?"

"You called me Katie."

"It was the name of Enid's favorite doll when she was young. I don't know, it was the first thing I thought of."

"But why were you in such a rush to get out of there?"

"I was afraid she'd recognized you."

"Recognized me?"

"From... from the news."

Blood drains from my face. "I'm on the news?" I slap my forehead. "Oh, Jesus, of course I'm on the news. I'm wanted for murder."

"Sorry. But yeah, you're on the news. Although they haven't come out and said you killed him. They're calling you 'a person of interest.'"

"That's what they say when they want to trick you into coming in. You think you're going in to provide evidence, and then they manipulate you into confessing."

"First of all, how the hell would you know that? And second of all, you didn't do anything, so you have nothing to confess."

"Somehow that doesn't make me feel any better."

Heath's face goes pale. He scans the surrounding street, at the milling pedestrians and the traffic that crawls along beyond them.

"What? What's wrong?" I touch his arm.

"Do you hear that?"

In the distance, a police siren wails.

I swallow. "Do you think she figured it out?"

"I don't know, but I think we better get the hell out of here before we find out."

THIRTY-TWO

WE GET into the subway before we see any trace of the cops, but the whole time we're riding the train back to the lot where we'd left the car, I expect the subway to do an emergency stop, for a SWAT team to bust in through the doors, guns blazing. I shake my knee up and down so hard that Heath puts his hand on my thigh and tells me, under his breath, to cool it.

As scary as it is riding the subway, coming back up from the underground is even worse. I climb the stairs to the carpark in abject terror. Are they already waiting for us? Surrounding Heath's car, guns drawn?

But all my fears are for naught. The car park is busy, but there aren't any police around, just a single uniformed security guard who doesn't give us more than a cursory glance as we walk toward the Camry.

"Do you want to go back to the motel?" he asks when we're safely ensconced inside.

I nod. I want to cry. All that risk today and we're still no closer to finding Taylor. Heath keeps silent during the drive. When we get to the motel, I try to convince him to go straight home, but he insists on walking me back to my room.

I get another pinch of worry right as I unlock the door — what are we going to find inside? — but the room is exactly as we left it. No daily housekeeping here.

"You can go now," I announce, stripping off the mint green coat. I want to put my old jeans back on. A person can only handle so much pink in one day.

"You need to eat something."

"No, I don't."

"You haven't eaten since breakfast."

"I'm not hungry."

"I'm going to go pick something up for you. I'll be back in twenty minutes or so."

There's no point in arguing, so I don't. As soon as he's gone, I take off the jeans and pull my own back on. That's better. I leave on the Chai Harder t-shirt — it's actually kind of cute. I lie on the bed and stare at the ceiling for a while and decide to turn on the TV and check out the local news. I've never seen my own face staring back at me from the television before, so hey, that'll be something.

But even though I flip through all the basic cable channels on offer, there's nothing. It's too early for the evening news; we're still fully ensconced in the daytime talk show period. I watch part of a show that features a group of simpering women discussing whether yoga is better than pilates for achieving a 'tight booty.' I turn the television off in disgust.

A few minutes later, there's a knock at the door. Once

again, my heart rises into my throat, but before I can even check the peephole, a familiar voice rings out. "It's me."

I open the door to find Heath brandishing a fast-food bag and waxy take-away cup. In his other hand is a plastic grocery bag.

"You didn't have to do that," I say as he enters.

"I know. But if I didn't, you wouldn't eat, and I couldn't have that on my conscience."

He hands me the fast-food bag, and though I won't admit it, the smell of the golden hot French fries is already making my mouth water. He dumps the plastic shopping bag on the stand with the television.

"I also brought you water, granola bars, and a box of Twinkies. You still like those?"

"I don't think I've eaten one since I was about twelve, but yeah. Thanks."

"I remember coming home one day and you and Enid were sitting at the kitchen table, cramming them down your throats like you'd been on a deserted island with no food for six months."

I smile at the memory. We'd wanted a snack on the way home from school, but instead of stopping for an ice cream cone the way we usually did, we'd instead gone to the grocery store and bought an entire box of Twinkies. We took them back to Enid's and gorged ourselves in her kitchen. I can still picture the open box in front of us, discarded wrappers around us like the detritus of some bacchanalian orgy of processed foods. The Connollys' house was so normal compared to my own that I reveled in it. Even the groceries were so banal they were wondrous. Enid couldn't see it; to her, it was like asking a fish to appreciate water. But to me, to someone who'd been dying of thirst, it was a revelation. A salvation.

"Thank you," I say again. "I hope the police aren't following you. It won't take them long to figure out why you're carting groceries and takeout to a shady motel."

"I didn't see anyone. And when they came to the house, they mostly spoke to Mom and Enid. I assume Enid told them we didn't really know each other that well. I only got a couple of cursory questions about whether I'd seen you recently, whether you'd said or done anything strange. I told them Malice has always been strange."

I punch him lightly in the arm. "Thanks, Heath." My voice is soft and threatens to break.

"You're welcome. I'll be back in the morning, okay?"

When Heath leaves, I tear open the fast-food bag and rip into the fries, then the burger, then eat two of the Twinkies. I might have denied being hungry, but clearly there's no problem with my appetite. Or maybe I just like the distraction.

But once I'm done eating, I have nothing else to do. No phone, no internet, no laptop. I turn the television back on, hoping to catch the evening news.

It's a few minutes to six, so I sit through a few mind-numbing commercials before the familiar eighties synth intro of the New York One nightly news comes on. I sit up, leaning toward the screen like a sunflower.

The top story is about a toddler who drowned in the Hudson earlier today. The details are tragic, but I can't keep the macabre grin off my face. Maybe that means I'm not news anymore.

But my relief is short-lived. As soon as the anchors wrap up the story, a picture of Weston Chambers flashes on screen.

"Police are still investigating the death of real estate developer and notorious playboy Weston Chambers," recites the male anchor, an airbrushed blowhard named Patrick Fairweather. "Chambers' body was discovered at The Grant Hotel last Friday, where police said he had been stabbed multiple times. We take you now to Tara Quinn, who's got more on this story."

The camera cuts to a blonde in a large, dim room. She mutters something off camera and tucks her hair behind her ear before realizing she's live.

"Good evening Patrick and Patricia," she says, in a bright, clear voice. "I'm here at 56 Water Street, in a building recently purchased by the Chambers Development Corporation."

Blood drains from my face. I recognize that space — it's the same warehouse Taylor and I broke into the other day. This can't be good.

"As you know, police have been searching for a young woman named Alice Brewster, a former employee of The Grant Hotel. Police haven't said whether they suspect her of the murder, only that she's a person of interest in the investigation."

My face flashes on the screen, sullen and slightly blurry. It's the ID photo from my passcard at The Grant.

"Now, here's where things get interesting, Patrick. I've

learned exclusively that Ms. Brewster was recently picked up vandalizing this very warehouse."

The camera pans the warehouse, showing off the spray-painted artwork that Taylor and I created. Seeing our slogans blared across the television is a punch to the gut. *'Weston Chambers is a rapist,'* I read again, feeling sick.

"Strong words," Patrick coos. "Do we know whether Weston Chambers may have ever assaulted Ms. Brewster?"

"We don't know that," the correspondent answers. "And there's no evidence of it; police say no charges were ever filed against Chambers, nor did they ever receive any complaints."

Of course not, I want to scream. Because everyone was bribed and intimidated into keeping quiet.

"So what do we think, then? A one-night stand gone wrong?"

"It's certainly possible. It's no secret that Weston Chambers was a handsome, rich, available man. He's been linked to actresses, singers, socialites — you name it, Patrick."

"A man after my own heart," he chuckles. "So is this act of vandalism the reason police are searching for Alice Brewster?"

"It's possible," says Tara, tucking her blonde hair behind her ear again. "Police are being tight-lipped about the investigation, but they've confirmed that Alice Brewster is a former employee of The Grant, so she may have come into contact with him there."

"Fascinating stuff, Tara," he says. "You have to wonder if this is another example of the #metoo movement taken too far."

"Absolutely, Patrick," she agrees. "I've also been advised

that police located a backpack containing close to ten thousand dollars in cash at Ms. Brewster's home on Staten Island. It's unclear what she was intending to use the money for, but it certainly raises many more questions."

"Indeed, it does. You'll continue to follow this story for us, won't you, Tara?"

"I'm on it, Patrick." Tara flashes the camera a grin that's a cross between flirtatious and predatory. "In the meantime, the public are advised to be on the lookout for Alice Brewster. She's described as being five-feet, four inches tall, approximately a hundred and ten pounds, with shoulder-length blonde hair and brown eyes..."

The screen flashes to my picture again. I turn the television off. I can't take any more of this. Beyond the fear at seeing my face splashed across the nightly news, there's also a boiling rage. How could they so willfully twist what happened? *A one-night stand gone wrong? The #metoo movement taken too far?* How could they paint Weston as a playboy, a word which conjures up images of a Gatsby-era cad, clad in white linen pants and tossing back a cocktail? Weston Chambers was a predator, pure and simple. He knew that his money, his status, his male-ness all gave him power, and he chose to use that power to hurt people. To destroy them.

My stomach roils again, and I bolt for the bathroom. The burger, fries, and Twinkies all come up in a violent rush. Even once they've been evacuated from my body, I still can't stop heaving. I push up bile and then spit and finally just air, and then I collapse backward onto the cool tile floor, sweating.

Eventually, I crawl back to the bed. My body feels depleted, but I can't think about touching any of the remaining food that Heath brought. I crack open a bottle of water and lie on top of the sheets, staring at the ceiling and counting the water stains.

In the silence of my motel room, I have nothing to do but think. But it's not Weston that I think about. It's Taylor. I replay every single moment we spent together, trying to find something, anything, to latch onto. Some snippet of information, some tiny kernel that will help me find her.

But I'm also searching for a sign. Anything that might indicate how twisted she was, why she would want to hurt me like this. She'd seemed so normal when I met her. Attractive. Inviting, even. Like someone you wanted to be around. She made me like her. She made me want *her* to like *me*.

I try to parse out what made her so appealing. Her personality, yes, sure. She was outgoing, bubbly. Wild, in a way. Willful. Powerful.

That's closer to the truth, I think. Powerful. She owned herself. Every piece of her — her body, her mind, her value, her opinions. The way she'd so easily clocked that guy in the alley when she thought he was assaulting the girl he was with. The way she'd felt no need to apologize when we realized our mistake. There was something magnetic about that. She was without apology. Without shame.

Without shame. Yes, that's it. I never once heard her sound even remotely apologetic for anything about herself. Taylor didn't break for anyone — not for you, not for herself. She was rock solid.

But not quite, I realize. Because there was once — one single time — when she seemed to choke on something. That was when she mentioned growing up in Ithaca. That was the only time I'd ever heard anything other than her usual ballsy bluster.

Ithaca.

Is it possible that Ithaca's the one truth that slipped out between all the lies?

It's worth a shot, isn't it?

Because it might be the only shot I have.

THIRTY-THREE

IN THE MORNING, Heath arrives bearing another delivery of coffee and breakfast sandwiches. I'm already dressed in Enid's pink jeans and another cartoon t-shirt, this one featuring a pink-frostinged, color-sprinkled donut with a cute smile and the words *Donut Worry, Be Happy*. I'm bouncing on my toes as he unloads the food, a rather unusual amount of enthusiasm for me.

"Alice, what's going on?" Heath eyes me up and down. "You're kind of freaking me out."

"I had an idea. I think I might know how we can find Taylor."

"Oh, yeah? That's great. What is it?"

"Ithaca."

"Ithaca? Like, the city?"

"Yeah. She said she grew up there. And I think it might have been the truth. The way she said it was... I don't know. It was different. It's hard to explain. It bothered her somehow."

"Ithaca." He rubs his jaw. "Okay. So what do you think—"

"She's twenty-five. Same age as me. So I'm thinking we go through the yearbooks, see if we can find her. At least we could get a last name. That would give us more options in terms of how to track her down. Maybe we could even find her on Facebook," I add, even though I'm not optimistic about that part. Taylor had gone to a lot of trouble to cover her tracks. Having a public social media presence seems unlikely.

Heath pulls out his phone and starts scrolling. "Okay, it looks like there's one main public high school for Ithaca. Maybe a half dozen if we count the surrounding areas, charter schools, et cetera. Let's see if any of them have their yearbooks online."

He sits on the bed and I flop down right next to him, leaning into his shoulder so I can see the screen. None of the schools have digital yearbooks on their websites, but we find a social networking site for alumni that promises digital copies of all the yearbooks.

"I'll sign up," I offer, but Heath shakes his head.

"It's probably better if I do it. We don't know if they're tracking your online activity. Plus, you need to pay with a credit card."

I relent, even though what I really want to do is rip the phone out of his hands. It takes him forever to key in his info and get onto the site.

"So, if she's twenty-five years old, she probably graduated in, what? 2012?"

"Let's check a few years' worth — 2010 to 2014."

"Works for me."

We work methodically. We start with the main Ithaca high school and open the earliest yearbook. We flip through the graduating class, looking for anyone named Taylor. Since it's Heath's phone, I let him do most of the scanning. I pace the room. Each time he finds someone named Taylor, he yells "here!" and thrusts the phone at me. Each time, I grab it in breathless anticipation and hand it back to him, shaking my head. It's never her. There are at least half a dozen Taylors in Ithaca who graduated around that time, and none of them are my Taylor.

We take almost four hours to go through all the yearbooks, and at the end, we have nothing to show for it.

"Should we expand our search? Maybe she graduated later than that, or earlier. Could she have gone to a high school farther outside the city?"

I shake my head. "No clue. She could have been home-schooled for all I know. Damn," I hiss. "I really thought we had something."

"I know this is frustrating," Heath says, dropping his phone on the bed. "But we'll figure something out."

"Like what?" I say balefully, aware I'm being childish and unhelpful but with no idea how to stop myself. "I'm out of ideas here, Heath."

"Me, too," he admits. "But something will come to us."

He lays backward on the bed and closes his eyes, pressing his fingers to his temples. I grab his phone. I flip through the most recent yearbook he'd been checking, skimming through the graduating class again. They're all wearing cardinal red gowns, their smiles eager and hopeful. Well, except for the ones who've tried to keep their faces determined and serious, but even those have a sort of youthful optimism to them. I try to remember if I ever felt that hopeful about the future, but I can't. I swipe through page after page of these kids, their faces blending in to one another as I scroll.

"Come on, Taylor," I mutter. "Where are you?"

And then... I don't believe it... *there she is.*

"Heath!" I swat at his leg and he sits up. I thrust the phone in front of him. "That's her! That's Taylor."

He scans the faces. "I don't see her."

I zoom in on the face. The hair is blonder and straightened to within an inch of its life, the lipstick is dark, and the eyeliner is even darker, but there's no denying that this is her. Taylor, seven years ago.

"Her name's not Taylor," Heath points out.

"Samantha Dennings," I read. We look at each other for a minute, before my eyes are drawn back to the picture.

Taylor. I run my finger over her photo. *Even your name was a lie. But now I've found you. And I'm going to figure out what the hell you did.*

"Tell us your secrets, Samantha Dennings," I whisper, tapping the phone.

THIRTY-FOUR

AS I SEARCH, my excitement is quickly muted. Samantha Dennings doesn't have a profile on the alumni site, nor is she on Facebook, Instagram, or any other social media site we check. Google doesn't turn up anything useful, either. There are quite a few Samantha Dennings out there, but none of them are the one we're looking for.

After an hour, I throw the phone down on the bed and groan. "We're not getting anywhere."

Heath rests backward on his hands, stretching out his long torso. "What about a private investigator? Or a skip tracer? There are people out there whose job it is to deal with this exact scenario. Finding people who don't want to be found."

"Maybe." I consider this, but the idea of engaging a stranger isn't one I can really entertain. Wouldn't they have some sort of obligation to turn me in? There are a total of two people in the world I trust right now, and both of them are in this room. "It seems risky, though. Not to mention expensive."

"Do you have any other ideas?" Frustration drips through his voice, but I ignore it. I don't really blame him. I'm frustrated as hell and this is my own mess.

We're both quiet, thinking for a few minutes. Heath turns his body toward me. "What if we start with what we know?" he asks.

"What do you mean?"

"Well, we know she graduated from high school in Ithaca. That's the only thing we're really sure on."

"Right."

"So... maybe we start there."

"What, you mean go to Ithaca?"

"Why not? Maybe we could figure out where she went from there. We might even find people there who know her, or who've kept in touch with her."

"That's true." The idea is starting to excite me, and not just because of the possibility that someone there might know how to get in touch with her. This is the first lead I've had on the *real* Taylor. Samantha Dennings is the person beneath all the lies, and I have an almost insatiable desire to know more about her. Who is she? What does she want? What's driving her?

"Let's do it."

"Great." Heath stands, jingling his keys.

"You mean now?"

He stares at me. "Do you have something better to do?"

I look around the motel room, which might not be much

but has represented relative safety for the last two days. "I guess not."

"Then let's go find this Samantha Dennings person. Let's get you some answers."

I don't bother checking out of the Sunset Motel, since I assume we'll be back late tonight or tomorrow at the latest. Still, I pack up all my stuff and take it with us just in case. Heath sets his phone to give us directions straight to the school Taylor — *Samantha* — went to, and then we're off. We don't talk much on the way, but I'm grateful for his presence. I don't know where I'd be without him. Probably still running around Staten Island in my socks, hiding in dumpsters and freezing to death.

That, or already in jail.

The drive takes forever, and the entire time, I'm so antsy that I could crawl right out of my own skin. I distract myself by looking at the high school's website on Heath's phone. When we finally pull up in front of Ithaca High School, my nerves really kick in.

Heath parks, and for a few minutes, we sit there and stare at the building. It looks eerily similar to my own high school — sprawling red brick surrounded by grassy fields and paved parking lots. There's absolutely nothing special about it, and certainly nothing that indicates it would have ever been home to the duplicitous monster known as Samantha Dennings.

"What's the plan?" Heath asks. "I saw you looking through the yearbook again on my phone."

"I was comparing the teachers back then to the current faculty list. There are about a dozen from Taylor's year that are still teaching here."

"Good thinking. So we'll start with one of them. Should we pick one at random?"

"Actually, there's a theater class here. And the teacher is still working. I thought we could start with him. I'd be willing to bet money that Taylor took his class."

"Great. Let's do it."

"Let's do it," I agree. I fling the car door open and jump out. If I don't do this now, I'm going to lose my nerve.

Inside the school, we locate the front office, which isn't hard, since it's right inside the main doors. It's past four o'clock, and the school is quiet. I'm worried we won't find anyone in the office, but as soon as we open the door, an electronic bell chimes and a pointy-looking woman torpedos out of a back room and straight toward us.

"Can I help you?" Her voice is as sharp as her features.

"We're looking for Mr. Tom Thibault."

"He'll be in the auditorium."

"Where can we find the auditorium?"

She eyes us suspiciously.

"He's expecting us," I lie. "We're from the university. We're assisting with some technical specs on the *Hamlet* production."

"Oh, all right." She gives us directions and waves us off.

"How'd you know they were doing *Hamlet*?" Heath whispers once we're out of earshot from the office.

"It's a high school. Every high school does *Hamlet*."

We slip into the auditorium unnoticed. On stage, a kid in

a cape holds up a plastic skull and gazes at it mournfully. At least, I'm hoping it's plastic. In the front row sits Tom Thibault. I recognize him from the yearbook photos. He wears a pale purple plaid shirt and khakis and sits with one leg draped over the other, his foot bouncing up and down at a manic pace. He holds a sheaf of papers, which he consults and makes notations on as the kids work through one of the later scenes in the play.

Heath and I slip into seats in the back row and wait out the rest of the rehearsal. It's painful, but not as bad as I'm expecting. Tom Thibault gives considered and patient advice to the students, and they respond enthusiastically to his direction. I try to imagine Taylor up on that stage. Was she the same star back then as she is now? Or was Samantha Dennings still coming into her own?

When Tom finally dismisses the students, it takes another half hour for them to gather their things and finally disperse their conversation groups. A few of them notice us on their way out, but no one says a thing. When the teacher is the only one left in the room, Heath and I stand. He can't get to the exit without seeing us.

When he spots us, he does an exaggerated double-take, placing one hand over his heart. "You startled me."

"Sorry about that. My name is... Katie. This is my colleague Andrew. We're hoping to talk to you about a former student of yours."

"Sit," he says. "I have a few minutes. I'm not sure how much information I can give you, though. There have been so many over the years."

We sit back down in the two seats we'd previously

occupied, and Tom sits in the row in front of us, angling his body so he's facing us. He's younger than I thought he was, maybe mid-thirties. He must have been fairly new as a teacher when he taught Taylor. "Who's the student?"

"Her name is Samantha Dennings."

There's a flicker of something I don't quite catch, and a pensive look comes over his face. "Where did you say you were from, Katie? What's your interest in Samantha?"

"She's missing," I say. I'd rehearsed this in the car on the way up here. "And we're making a documentary about the case."

"A documentary?" His eyebrows shoot up theatrically.

"For Netflix," I add.

"Well, then." He takes off his glasses and polishes them on his shirttails before slipping them back on. "Have you got cameras, then?"

"Not with us. This is just an initial fact-finding mission. We want to see who would be good on camera."

"Ah, of course." He straightens. "What would you like to know?"

"Anything at all. How well do you remember Samantha Dennings?"

"Oh, very well. Let me see. She was a tremendous young woman."

"In what way?"

"She was an exceptional actress. Her senior year, we did *Romeo and Juliet*. She was Juliet, of course. She was exceptional. Exceptional. Soulful beyond her years. But she would be, wouldn't she? After everything she'd been through. That poor girl."

Heath and I exchange a look. "Could you elaborate on that? What had she been through?"

He hesitates, for the first time unsure about divulging information about a former student to two complete strangers. "Did you say she was missing?"

"She is. We became friends a few years ago, but we lost touch and I haven't been able to track her down. I can't get the police to take me seriously, so I found Andrew, here." I gesture to Heath. "He's a producer at Netflix. He wanted to help me get Samantha's story out. So any information you have would really help us out. Help Samantha, really."

He nods sagely. "Of course. Well, as I'm sure you know, Sam didn't have the easiest life. Her mother was — well, frankly, I'm not totally sure of the whole story there. I do know that Sam was in and out of foster care her whole life. It created rather a lot of instability for her, as you can imagine. I always felt that acting was what allowed her to escape. She was able to escape into these different roles, you see. Sometimes, watching her on stage, you felt as if you were getting your first and only glimpse of the real Samantha. And then the curtain would close and she'd be gone again. Poof." He makes an exploding gesture with his hands and looks wistfully off into the distance.

I wonder if he's already imagining himself in our so-called documentary. I have the overwhelming urge to punch him, even though he's technically giving us the very information we need.

"Did Sam have a lot of friends?" Heath asks, saving me from doing anything I might regret.

"She had... let's call it a large social circle. But friends, no.

I expect she didn't let people get that close to her. As a defense mechanism, you see. It's wonderful that you and she became friends," he says to me.

"Yes, it was... wonderful," I echo. "She's a very special person."

"I always saw that," he agrees. "I always, always saw that. Her specialness."

I'm sure you did. "Is there anyone we could talk to who might have kept in touch with her after high school? Anyone from her social circle? Boyfriends? Anyone at all?"

He shrugs. "You might try Caitlin Connors. I think they were friends. As for boyfriends, I'm afraid I didn't keep up with that sort of gossip. I believe she was close with a young man named Phillip Huxley. Other than that, I can't say."

I make a mental note of the names. "Thank you for your time, Mr. Thibault," I say standing.

He stands as well. "So, am I in?"

"Are you in what?"

"The documentary."

"Yes, of course. The studio will be in touch," Heath says smoothly, before I can throat punch him. "I see a very big role for you."

"Oh, that's wonderful," he says, clapping his hands together. "I mean, anything to help Samantha, of course."

"Of course."

As Heath and I walk from the auditorium, Tom follows closely behind. He chuckles lightly as we all turn the same way toward the school's main entrance.

"Don't you hate when this happens?" he says. "You've

already said your farewells, and then you find yourself stuck walking in the same direction."

"I call it the long goodbye," Heath jokes.

"That's very good." He chuckles again. We reach the door and Thibault holds it open for us. "I'll be interested in what her foster family has to say about her. They knew her better than anyone, of course."

Of course. The foster family. "Right. Do you know how we can get in touch with them? Are they still in the city?"

"Oh, as far as I know, yes. She had several different foster situations over the years, but when she graduated, she was staying with the Hamilton family. They're on Linn Street, I believe. Near the cemetery. The father works out at the airport. Jim, I think his name is."

We part ways with Tom Thibault, thanking him again for his time and his information and promising 'the studio' will be in touch. When we're in the sanctity of Heath's Camry, I realize my entire body is buzzing with adrenaline.

"What do you think?" Heath asks as he starts up the car.

"I think I can't wait to meet the Hamiltons."

THIRTY-FIVE

HEATH SUGGESTS we get something to eat before crashing the Hamiltons' house, and since he's been such a good sport so far, I don't argue. We find a drive-thru not too far from the high school and get burgers, fries, milkshakes. I wonder if I'll ever eat a vegetable again.

"That visit was more fruitful than I thought it would be," Heath says as he pulls into the parking lot so we can chow down.

"Me, too," I admit. "Never underestimate a person's desire to end up on Netflix, I guess."

Heath grins. "That was inspired, I must say."

He passes me a cardboard container filled with piping hot fries and reaches for his phone. "Let's see what we can find out about the Hamiltons."

For once, luck is on our side. Jim Hamilton and his wife Shannon are all over Facebook. They're still foster parents, and their feeds are choked with photos of kids of all ages and ethnicities, with a healthy smattering of memes about parenting and 'the lord's work.' While we can't find an exact address, there are plenty of photos of the exterior of their house. If we drive up and down Linn Street and the surrounding area, we should be able to find it.

As we unwrap our burgers, we check out the other names Tom Thibault gave us. Caitlin Connors, a friend of Sam's, and Phillip Huxley, her possible boyfriend.

Neither lead pans out. Caitlin Connors lives in Wales and seems to have been there for at least five years. From what we can piece together from her social media, she went over on a work visa years ago and fell in love with a Welsh guy. Got married and never came back to the States. So it's unlikely that she and Sam are still in touch.

Phillip Huxley is even less promising; he's dead. Motorcycle accident about three years ago. His social feeds are all condolence messages, a new crop of which pop up every year on his birthday. I scan through them, but there are none from Taylor or Samantha or any other blonde who looks like her.

"I sure hope the Hamiltons can give us something," Heath says as he crumples up the wrapper from his burger and tosses the bag into the back seat.

"Me too. Ready?"

"Let's do it."

While Heath drives, I review the photos of the Hamiltons' house. In addition to their own home, they've posted pictures of the yard, which show off the neighbors across the road, and using Google Earth we're able to piece together roughly where on Linn their house is located. Once we orient ourselves on the street, it takes all of five minutes to locate the two-story slate blue home.

"People never consider what they share on social media." I shake my head. "You'd think with all those vulnerable kids, they'd care at least a little about privacy."

"Don't complain," Heath says. "That lack of concern for privacy might work in our favor."

I can't argue with that. We watch the house for a few minutes, but there's no sign of life from within or without. There's no car in the driveway, but that doesn't necessarily mean anything, since there's also an attached garage.

"Shall we?" Heath asks.

Up close, the house is less pristine than it looked from the street. The lawn is neatly mowed but choked with weeds, and the blue siding is cracked in places. But the front porch has a rocking chair and a pot of mums, a little red wagon, and a pair of child-sized rubber boots. It looks like a nice, normal house.

I ring the bell while Heath hovers behind me. I plan to use the same story I'd used at the high school — that Sam is missing and that we're doing research for a documentary — and I mentally rehearse my introduction while we wait.

When no one answers, I ring the bell a second time. After a minute, there's still no answer, so I try banging on the door. Nothing.

"Maybe they're not home yet."

I try the doorknob, just to see, and find it locked. I look despairingly at Heath.

"Let's wait a bit," he suggests. "Maybe they'll be home soon."

We retreat to the Camry, where we sit in silence. Minutes pass, and then an hour, then two. Finally, we have to admit they're not coming home anytime soon. It's dark and, even if they showed up in the next five minutes, I can't imagine we'd garner any favor if we knocked on their door at nine o'clock at night. Not with all the kids they've got.

"We can try again tomorrow," Heath says, sensing my disappointment. "First thing in the morning. We'll sit out here all day if we have to."

"Where are we going to stay tonight?"

"I'll get us a motel room," he says. "I'll put it under my name. It's a risk, but we don't have much choice."

I can't argue with that.

We settle on a basic Super 8, which is a palatial resort compared to the Sunset Motel. I wait in the car while Heath checks in. Even with my new hair and new clothes, I'm nervous about being recognized. The fewer people who see me, the better.

When he's done, Heath comes back out to get me and we carry a few things up to our third-floor room.

"I only got us the one room," he says. "But I asked them for two double beds. Said I like to have room to spread out my stuff."

"Thanks. I'm sure it's fine."

But when Heath pushes open the door, we're greeted by a single queen-sized bed.

"I'll go back," Heath offers. "Ask them for a different room."

"It's fine." I'm suddenly too tired to care.

"Do you want me to — should I sleep on the floor? I don't mind."

I look around the room incredulously. Where exactly does he think he'd sleep? The room is tiny, and there's barely room for the bed as it is. There are no nightstands, just sconces mounted on the wall on either side of the bed. The TV is also wall-mounted on the other side of the room.

I roll my eyes and flop down on the edge of the bed. "Heath, it's fine. After everything I've been through in the last week, sharing a bed with Enid's brother is pretty low on my list of worries."

"Right." He kicks off his shoes and lies down on the bed next to me, but as close to the edge as he can get.

I lay my head down on the pillow, my back to Heath. My eyes are already drifting closed.

"Hey, Malice?"

"What?" I don't bother opening my eyes.

There's a pause, and then, "I'm really sorry this is happening to you."

"Thanks. Me too."

He's quiet again for another few minutes. I'm drifting off to sleep when his voice cuts in again.

"I meant to tell you, Enid went to your house last night. To check on your mom."

My eyes snap open and I turn to face him. "How is she? Is she scared? Does she know what's going on?"

"She's worried, yeah. But she's managing. I think she blames herself."

"What? Why? This has nothing to do with her."

"I think... I don't know. I think she feels you were keeping things from her because you felt like you couldn't lean on her. She has this idea that if you could have talked to her, she could have helped somehow. That's what Enid says, anyway."

"That's crazy."

"I know. But that's mothers. Mine would feel the same way."

As if I needed any more guilt about all the lives I'm ruining. I bury my face in my hands.

"Hey," Heath says. "I didn't mean to upset you." His hand rests against my shoulder and then he's rubbing it, tentatively but gently.

"I don't blame you. I blame myself."

"Alice, this isn't your fault. This Taylor person is crazy. I don't know why she targeted you—"

"She targeted me because I was an easy mark," I spit.

He raises his eyebrows. "Alice, of all the things I've ever thought of you as, an 'easy mark' is not one of them."

But I'm already shaking my head. "She saw something in me. Some pathetic, needy core." I hate myself for getting sucked into her orbit. It wouldn't have happened if I'd been stronger. If I'd only ignored her that day at El Diablo.

"Don't talk about yourself that way," Heath says.

His voice is gentle, which only makes me feel worse. I don't need anyone's pity.

"You don't even know me," I say. "Not really."

"I do," he says. "Or at least I like to think I do."

His words sit between us for a few minutes. Heath props himself up on one elbow. He's grinning. "Remember when Enid was getting bullied by those seventh-grade girls? You set a literal trap in the playground for them — using, what was it? A ten-dollar bill?"

"A five." I can't help the small grin that touches my lips. "Those bitches were cheap."

"Right. And after you'd lured them behind the school, you beat one of them up and threatened the rest of them. They never touched Enid again."

"Technically, I didn't beat anyone up," I say, but I can't help but think of the whole thing fondly. Brittany, Kyla, and Anne-Marie had made Enid's life a living hell for an entire month before I'd had enough of seeing my friend crying in the girls' bathroom every day. Revenge was easy; those bitches never even saw it coming. I'd taped a piece of fishing line to a five-dollar bill and used it to lure them to the back of the playground, behind the slide. They'd chased after it like white mice chasing cocaine in one of those lab experiments. And even though they were two years older and at least six inches taller than me, I hadn't been scared. I hid up at the top of the slide with a stockpile of rocks and hit them from above. It was an ambush. Brittany had needed four stitches in her forehead where I'd caught her with a rock. The other two ran away like the scared, pathetic people they were.

No one messed with Enid after that, and no one messed with me, either. The two-week suspension was more than worth it.

"Enid practically worshipped you after that," Heath

chuckles. "Trust me, she doesn't think you're pathetic. And neither do I."

My smile quickly fades. I know he's trying to be nice, but I've changed a lot since fifth grade. "Things were different with Taylor. I think she saw something in me. Something broken."

"What do you mean? What did she see?"

I don't answer. Instead, I turn so my back is to him again. I can feel him breathing behind me, waiting for me to respond, but I can't do it.

We lie in silence for so long that I think he's drifted off to sleep. The room is dark, save for a slant of red light that glows through the blinds from the motel's exterior sign. The only sound is the dull roar of the highway traffic in the distance.

"I lied about knowing Weston Chambers," I whisper into the silence.

Heath stirs beside me but doesn't say anything. Is he awake? Asleep? I don't care. I want to say the words.

"He was a guest at the hotel where I worked. He raped me. They paid me to keep quiet about it. Five hundred thousand dollars. That's what I'm worth. A half a million dollars. Except Taylor took that from me, too. Or Sam did. Whatever the hell her name is."

"Alice," Heath breathes. "I'm so sorry. You should have said something."

His body curls behind mine, his arms snaking around my middle. I freeze. His touch is gentle, but it's so unfamiliar, so foreign and strange, that I don't know what to do about it. When his lips touch the back of my neck, I bolt out of the bed.

"What are you doing?"

"I'm sorry." He sits up, rubbing his face. "I thought..."

"You thought what? That you could make it all better? That I just need the love of a good man and all my sad little girl wounds will be magically healed?"

"No, Alice, Jesus. I'm not trying to heal you. You don't need to be healed."

"You're damn right, I don't."

"I'm sorry. I really am. Can you get back into bed? I promise I won't touch you."

I sit on the edge of the bed, my back half to him.

"Why'd you tell me that stuff?" he asks. There's no accusation in his voice, just genuine curiosity.

"I don't know. Because I wanted you to see the real me."

He chews on this for a bit. "I think that's why I reached for you. Because I *do* see the real you. And I like you. I always have. I wanted you to know the way I see you hasn't changed."

"Yeah, well. You could have chosen your moment a little better." I offer him a half smile. Maybe a quarter.

"I guess I could have. I'm sorry."

"We should get some sleep. Tomorrow is probably going to be a long day."

He holds up the covers, and I hesitate only a second before slipping back under them.

Beside me, Heath falls into a deep sleep almost immediately. His breathing goes steady. He's as still as a corpse. I lay on my back beside him, trying to mirror his breathing, but sleep doesn't come as easily for me. I lay awake for a long time. Eventually, Heath rolls over onto his side, his back to me. I stare at that broad expanse, still clad in the same t-shirt he'd been wearing earlier. I inch closer to his solid form, until I'm curled up right behind him, like a mouse behind a wall. I fall asleep that way, my breath warm in my own face as it bounces off his back.

THIRTY-SIX

WHEN I WAKE UP, Heath is in the shower. I wipe the sleep from my eyes and try to erase the memory of last night from my mind. It doesn't go easily.

I dread the moment he's going to saunter out of the bathroom, but when he does, he's fully dressed and toweling off his dark hair. He shows no hint that he's dwelling at all on what happened last night. I don't know whether that's a good thing or a bad thing.

"I thought we could hit the drive-thru for breakfast and then go right to the Hamiltons' house. We might be able to catch them before they go to work for the day."

"What if they're on vacation?"

"We'll deal with that later. We have no reason to think they aren't going to be home."

He's right, I know. I grab a quick shower and pull on the same clothes I wore yesterday. They're starting to get pretty ripe, and I make a mental note to ask if we can stop at a Walmart or something on the way back to the city.

After we've picked up coffees and bagels, Heath drives us back to Linn Street. This time, there's a pickup truck parked in the driveway.

"That's obviously not the family car," I muse, "but maybe this means the dad's home, at least."

"That'll do." Heath and I walk up to the front door and ring the bell. Again, no one answers.

"Come on," I mutter. I ring the bell again.

The door opens a crack and slowly widens to reveal a toddler holding a sippy cup. She has brown skin and soft, wild hair and is wearing a pink dress with yellow leggings. Actually, she's dressed a bit like me.

"Hi, I'm looking for Mr. or Mrs. Hamilton," I say.

She blinks up at me, grinning around the mouthpiece of her sippy cup.

"Is your mom or dad home?" I try. "Shannon and Jim?" I don't know how this child refers to her foster parents, or if they're possibly her biological parents.

One of those must get through to her, because she spins on her heel and runs down the hallway. "Shanny! Shanny!"

A harried-looking woman appears around the corner. "What is it, Rosie?"

She sees Heath and me standing there and stops. "Hi. Can I help you? Go into the kitchen, Rosie. Your eggs are ready."

"Hi, Mrs. Hamilton? My name is Katie, and this is my colleague, Andrew. We're hoping we could talk to you about one of your former foster kids."

"What's this about?" Her eyes narrow suspiciously. "Are you Social Services?"

"No, not at all. We're, uh, we're making a documentary."

"Not interested."

She tries to close the door on us, but I jam my shoulder against it. I make a split-second decision.

"I'm sorry; that's not true. We're not making a documentary. I'm trying to find Samantha Dennings."

"Sam," she breathes. She eases up the pressure on the door a little. "Why are you looking for her?"

"She's... a friend of mine. And some stuff happened. I just want to make sure she's okay, but I can't find her. I was hoping you might have some insight."

She sighs. She considers us, then shrugs and opens the door wider. "Come on in. I have a few minutes before I've got to get this lot off to school. I'll be upfront with you, though, I don't know where she is."

I try not to let my disappointment show as we follow her into a cluttered living room. Toys are strewn across the floor, along with at least two tablets in brightly colored plastic cases. A copy of the third Harry Potter book is laying open on the coffee table. But despite the mess, the room is comfortable — the sofa is a big L-shaped sectional, and two equally comfy-looking chairs sit across from it. A TV is mounted over the fireplace.

Heath and I sit on the couch, while Shannon takes one of the chairs opposite. She's much the same as the home's decor — slightly chaotic, but warm and comforting. Her white-blonde hair is pulled back in a messy ponytail, and, though her skin is aged, her face is still pretty, her blue eyes kind. She's wearing a pink sweatshirt and pale blue jeans. Around her neck is a necklace — a turtle with a small emerald stone on its shell.

"When's the last time you heard from Sam?" I try.

Shannon shakes her head. "Not since she turned eighteen. Almost as soon as she aged out of the system, she was gone."

Damn. So it's very unlikely we're going to get anything useful here. They haven't heard from Sam in years. "She never said where?"

"No. But she wouldn't have. We tried to make her comfortable here, to make her feel loved and supported, but Sam was a tough case. She'd been through so much, and she was already seventeen when she came here. If we'd been with her earlier, maybe we could have helped more, but she was already so closed in on herself."

Sounds ring out from the kitchen. The clattering of dishes, a high-pitched giggle, the sizzle of bacon. "Did you have other foster children at the time? Was there anyone she was close to?"

"We did, yes, but no one Sam was close to. They were all quite a bit younger, and, like I said, she was very closed in on herself. Did you say she disappeared?"

"Sort of. I haven't been able to get in touch with her. None of her neighbors have seen her, and she hasn't been at work." It's somewhat of a lie, but an innocent enough one.

"I'm not surprised," Shannon says with a nod. "Sam was always disappearing. The first time it happened, we thought she'd run away, but we found her at a hotel downtown. She'd stolen a teacher's credit card and checked herself in."

Well, doesn't that sound familiar. I guess she learned that trick early on.

"And that happened more than once?"

"Not the credit card thing, but we'd find her in all kinds of places. She spent a couple nights sleeping at the bus station, or crashing with people she'd meet on the street. She used to tell them she was a backpacker and had lost her place to stay. People used to take pity on her and take her in."

"It sounds like she was a handful."

Shannon offers a small smile. "She was very creative. She had a great imagination, and I always thought she would have made a good actress. She loved her theater class at the high school. We even offered to enroll her in a prestigious New York City drama class the summer after graduation."

"What happened?"

"She agreed to do it. It was expensive, but we scrimped and saved for six months. We wanted to be able to do this for her. To show her that there were people in the world who were rooting for her."

"But she never went?"

"Oh, she went. For about two days. Then she dropped out. The school contacted us, but we never heard from her again. Since she was eighteen, Social Services wouldn't help us track her down, and the police here took a basic report but, as far as I know, they did frig all to find her. Pardon my French."

"Did she know anyone in New York?"

"Not that I'm aware of."

"What about her friends from high school?"

"What friends?"

"Caitlin Connors? Phillip Huxley?"

Shannon shakes her head. "They weren't really her friends. She hung out with them a few times, but it was more out of boredom than anything else. Sam didn't really have friends. Sam had Sam, and that was it."

"What about her life before she was placed with you?"

"It wasn't pretty," Shannon says, with a grim expression. "How much do you know?"

"A bit," I hedge. "But I'd like to hear your perspective on it."

"Sam got dealt a bad hand. I used to think all the time about what her life might have been like if she'd gotten a better start. I usually try not to dwell on that kind of thing, because these kids have all had a rough start, and it in no way precludes them from thriving as adults, if they can be cared for and supported in the way they need. But with Sam — I don't know. I guess I felt guilty that I could never really reach her."

"What specifically do you think affected her the most?" I prod. I feel bad for digging for information like this. Even though Taylor has been messing with my life and I have every right to information that'll allow me to track her down, it's different to be hearing about Sam Dennings. Although I know they're the same person, it feels like listening to salacious gossip about a stranger.

"Well, you know about her mother, right? There was no hope there. I hate to say that about someone, but after twenty years doing this, I've learned to call them like I see them. Sam's mother, Evangeline, was an addict. A total junkie. Heroin. She used to turn tricks to support her habit. She'd bring men back to that squalid apartment and have sex with them while Sam was forced to sleep under the bed."

My stomach turns. Beside me, Heath shifts.

"This went on for a while. Social Services took her away the first time when she was about three. She ended up in a good family — the Petersiks, Julie and Rod, I know them personally — but after about a year, Evangeline got clean and wanted her daughter back. They had to turn her back over. Don't get me wrong — I support reuniting children with their parents when it's in the best interest of the child. And if Evangeline had stayed clean, maybe things would have been different."

"But she didn't."

"No, she didn't. Within a year, she was back to her old tricks. Literally. Sam was five when she was taken away again."

"Another family?"

"Yes. This one lasted two years. Then..."

"Evangeline got clean again."

"You guessed it. This happened four or five times."

"Damn. That must be hard on a child."

"Exactly. In some ways, the back and forth is actually worse than being in one place, even if that place is miserable. When she was with a family, she was constantly wondering when her mother would take her back. When she was with her mother, she was constantly worried about being taken away again. That's no way to for a kid to live."

"No, it's not." I don't have to fake the sympathy in my voice. "Where was her father in all this?"

"Who knows? My understanding is that he was one of Evangeline's johns. He wasn't in the picture."

"Is there anything else you can tell us? What about the other families she was with? Would any of them have kept in touch with her?"

Shannon looks away. Her eyes go to the Harry Potter book, which she picks up and flips through before setting it back on the coffee table and examining her fingernails.

"Shannon?" I prod. I don't want to push her, but if there's information we can use, I want to know what it is.

Shannon is still focused on her nails which are, like the rest of her, short and no-nonsense. Heath and I exchange another glance.

"I don't want to speak badly about foster homes," she says finally. "There are good people in the foster care system. We've worked our whole lives to bring something to these children, to make sure they leave with something more than they came with."

I sense a 'but' coming, and sure enough, Shannon sighs.

"But look, the foster community is like anywhere else. There are bad apples that ruin the bunch."

I get the sense that I should keep my mouth shut and let her talk, so that's what I do.

"Sam mostly had good foster families. Or at least average ones. There were maybe some where she didn't get the attention she should have, ones where the parents had motive beyond helping kids who need it. But she did have one horrible experience, and that likely damaged her more than staying with her mother would have."

I already know what's coming — somehow, I just know it innately.

Shannon takes a deep breath. "Sam had one foster father who used to interfere with her."

My gut clenches.

"Interfere?" Heath asks, confused.

"He raped her, that's what you mean?" I push Shannon. I feel sick at how easily that word rolls off my tongue these days. "He molested her?"

She nods, her blue eyes pooling with tears, which she hastily wipes away with the back of her hand. "Yes. It's a tragedy when it happens to any child, but when it's an already-vulnerable foster child, I — I'd kill the bastard myself if he wasn't already dead."

"He's dead?" Of all the things she's said, this is the one that piques my interest the most.

"Cancer. About ten years ago. I pray to God that he suffered."

My excitement evaporates. I'd thought that maybe Sam had... but no. Cancer is pretty clear-cut.

"Shanny! Shanny!" Rosie, the toddler who'd opened the door for us, sprints into the living room. This time, she's got on a green jacket and red polka-dot rubber boots. She's carrying a backpack with a cartoon character I don't recognize on it.

"Hun?" A man appears at the doorway behind her. A thick beard covers half of his face. He's got another toddler perched on his hip, and behind him lurks a dark-eyed boy of about ten. "Are you free, or do you want me to drop the kids off? I'll have to take your van if I do."

"No, no, that's okay." Shannon stands up, brushing invisible lint off her jeans. She takes the toddler off her husband and kisses the top of his curly-haired head. "I'm afraid I'm out of time," she says to us.

"That's okay. Thank you so much for your help." We stand and walk with them to the front door. Once we're back in the Camry, Heath and I sit there for a few more minutes, both of us trying to process everything Shannon told us. We watch as the garage door opens and a minivan backs out. Shannon squints at us as she pulls out, and I offer what I hope is a friendly wave. She stays parked in the driveway beside the pickup.

"I think she's waiting for us to leave," Heath says.

"We better go, then." I can't help but smile. "She was nice, but I don't think I want to mess with her."

"I think you might be right." Heath starts up the car, and we pull away from the curb.

THIRTY-SEVEN

BEFORE WE LEAVE ITHACA, we stop at a Walmart so I can pick up a few essentials. Heath has to give me a couple hundred dollars, because I can't use my own credit card. I make it an in-and-out trip because I'm nervous about being around too many people, but I grab a couple pairs of jeans, some t-shirts, underwear, socks, a cheap pair of running shoes, a windbreaker, sunglasses, and a ball cap. I pay with Heath's money and duck into the public washroom so I can change clothes. I emerge feeling at least fifty percent better.

Heath looks me up and down when I return to the car where he's been waiting. The new clothes aren't as Easter Bunny-ish as the things I'd borrowed from Enid, but they also aren't as macabre as my usual black on black on grey on black wardrobe. I'm wearing regular blue jeans, a white t-shirt, and a purple sweater. I toss the bags in the back set and tuck the windbreaker, royal blue, down next to me, between the seat and the car door, so that I'll have it later.

We start the drive back to the city. I flit between radio

stations, trying to find a song that doesn't make me want to stick a straw into both my ears, and finally turn the whole thing off in a huff.

"You can plug my phone in," Heath offers. "I have a few playlists downloaded."

"That's okay."

In the silence, I mentally replay the conversation with Shannon. It makes me queasy and sad to think about what Sam went through, but when I try to reconcile it with the Taylor I met, the Taylor who killed Weston Chambers and tried to set me up for it, my brain goes fuzzy. It's like scrolling between two radio stations, where they're blending into each other, and I can't quite find the point where either of them are clear on their own.

"The thing I can't figure out," I announce to the silence of the car, "is *why me*. I get that Taylor — or Sam — had a rough upbringing. I get why she might be disturbed. I even get why maybe hearing about my rape might have triggered her somehow. But I don't get why *me*."

Heath shrugs. "Some people are just crazy, Alice. It probably wasn't anything to do with you at all."

"She didn't seem crazy."

"Well, you'd have to be, wouldn't you? To do something like this?"

"But it's so... random. She could have chosen anyone. Yet the plan itself was so calculated. She had everything worked out — the apartment, the phone. She'd even picked out a fake roommate, a fake ex-boyfriend. She even went to the trouble of stealing my wallet in advance. She had to have some reason to target me. She sought me out. Why?"

Heath doesn't have anything to offer. I stare out the window, watching the road and the scenery pass by as we get closer to the city. My brain turns the problem over and over, but I don't get any closer to an answer. I have no connection to Taylor, or to Samantha Dennings. We didn't grow up in the same area; we don't know any of the same people.

Only... what if we do?

"What if she worked at The Grant?" I wonder aloud.

"Wouldn't you have known her?"

"There were tons of people I never met there. And she could have worked there long before I did. We might not have overlapped at all." An idea comes to me, starts rolling itself into a ball in my mind, taking shape and gaining heft. "What if... what if Weston assaulted her, too? What if that, I don't know, triggered her somehow? What if she wanted to kill him, but didn't want to get the blame for it? So she found me. She knew we'd both have motive, so she made sure the evidence pointed to me instead of her."

Heath considers the idea. "It's possible, I guess."

"It's more than possible." I lean forward, excited. Everything is adding up. The hotel already knew Weston was dangerous — that's why they had the rule that two people had to clean the room at the same time. That means that before me, at least one other person had to have been assaulted. What if that person was Taylor?

"We're almost home," Heath says, gesturing to the Sunset Motel sign visible in the distance. "We can talk this out and figure out what to do next."

But I already know what to do next. I have to get in touch with Minnie, get her to find out whether anyone named

Samantha Dennings ever worked at The Grant. I'm sure that I already know the answer, but getting confirmation will be one more piece of evidence that I can go to the police with.

When we get to the Sunset Motel, I announce my plans to Heath.

"Let me come with you," he says.

I shake my head. "Minnie knows me. She's more likely to talk openly if I'm alone."

Heath doesn't look happy, but I can tell he sees the logic in it. I try not to let him see that the idea of riding the subway into Manhattan by myself is absolutely terrifying.

"You might as well go home," I insist. "Or go to work for a few hours. I'm sure the people in your life are starting to wonder what the hell is going on with you."

Again, I can tell that my words hit their intended mark. Heath reluctantly heads for the door.

"Be careful," he says before he leaves. I promise him I will.

Once he's gone, I expect to feel relieved. I'm not used to spending that much time with another human being. But instead, I feel strangely bereft.

It's still early, so I decide to hop in the shower before I go down to The Grant. After, I pull my new clothes back on, shove my knife and wallet into my pocket, and head out.

I'm heading down the stairs from my second-floor room when two police cruisers pull into the motel's parking lot.

"Shit." This is about me. I just know it. Somehow, in my gut, I know they're here because of me. I force myself to take deep breaths. I have to get out of here.

I double back up to the second floor before they can

notice me and zip around to the back. Thank God there are only two police units; they haven't surrounded the place. There's a second staircase at the back of the motel, at the opposite end of where my room is located, but it leads to the same parking lot. The only way to the street is via the front of the motel. The back of this place is wrapped in a ten-foot metal fence, on the other side of which is some kind of auto salvage shop.

But I can't stay up here. If they're really here for me, it won't be long before they hit the second floor, and once they do, there'll be no way out.

I make a split-second decision and sprint down the back staircase. The back of the motel is quiet, and I creep along to the end of the block of rooms so I can see into the parking lot. It's so quiet back here that I can almost think those cops were simply here for something routine, but when I poke my head around the edge of the building, two of them are scaling the stairs to the second floor, the other two standing guard at the bottom. No one is getting on or off the second floor without their notice.

I say a silent prayer of thanks that I wasn't in my room when they arrived. If I had been, there'd have been no escape. At least now I have a chance.

Maybe not much of one, though. There's no way to get through the parking lot without them seeing me, and no way to get to the road without crossing through the parking lot. I'm stuck back here.

My heart pounds in my chest as I press my body to the cinderblock wall of the motel. What do I do? How do I get out of here?

I have to figure something out, because in about a minute or so, they're going to loop around the second floor to the back of the motel where my room is. All they'd have to do is look down and they'd see me. They might not immediately recognize me with my new hair, but they're sure as hell going to take a second look at a suspicious woman lurking around the back of the motel where Alice Brewster is supposed to be staying.

The metal fence looms beside me. Beyond it, the salvage yard. There are plenty of places to hide amidst the scrap cars. But can I scale the fence? It's ten feet high and chain-link style. Not impossible, but...

I have no choice. I grab hold of the steel wire and pray that my years of scaling up and down the getaway tree outside my bedroom will serve me well.

The sleeve of my new windbreaker tears as I go over the top. One look up to the second floor of the Sunset Motel, and I see the cops rounding the corner. I don't have time to climb down. I let myself drop to the ground, then duck and roll behind the nearest scrap heap formerly known as a Jetta.

From my crouched position I can see the cops make their way down the open corridor, coming to a stop... right in front of my room. I knew they were here for me. I knew it.

But how did *they* know?

Heath and I have tried to be careful, but apparently not careful enough. Is it possible they've been tailing him?

Or maybe someone else saw me. I think of the peeled grape working in the front office, the creep who'd checked us in and demanded an extra few hundred bucks for keeping his mouth shut. Maybe he'd decided my money wasn't good enough.

But right now, the question of how the police found me isn't the most important one on my mind. The real question is...

What the hell do I do now?

Unfortunately, I have no time to dwell on it. Because right at that moment, something growls behind me, low and deep and menacing. I turn around, still in a crouch, and find myself face to face with a very large, very mean-looking Rottweiler.

THIRTY-EIGHT

THE FIRST THOUGHT that comes to my mind is — absurdly — *I've never seen teeth like that in my life.*

My second thought — far more rationally — is *dear God, I never want to* feel *teeth like that in my life.*

The animal snarls, and a line of drool drips down from its open jaw.

"Good doggy," I whisper. I back up a few inches, scared to move too suddenly in case I startle it. In case it decides I'm *prey.*

But the dog takes a few steps closer, closing the distance. It growls again, snapping its fierce jaw.

"Rhonda! Rhonda, you get back here." A man's panting voice comes from a few feet away. When he rounds the last crushed car and comes upon me, he stops. "What the hell are you doing here?"

The man facing me is an older guy, sixties maybe, wearing a pair of dark coveralls. The name tag on his breast pocket reads 'Larry.' His face is round, red, and weather-lined. The dog — Rhonda — snarls again.

I scramble to my feet, but stay hunched down low so I'm mostly hidden by the car. Even with this new threat, I'm still keenly aware of the greater threat waiting for me back at the Sunset Motel. "Nothing. Sorry. I'm just leaving."

"Ya know, we got this fence up for a reason." Larry gestures to the chain link surrounding us.

"I know, I just—"

"It means no trespassing."

"I'm sorry. I'll go now." I risk a quick glance at the motel. The two cops who'd been banging on my door are descending the staircase again. Is it my imagination, or is there a slump of defeat to their shoulders?

The old guy catches me looking and follows the direction of my gaze. He cracks a smile, revealing a missing canine tooth. "I get it. On the run, are ya? What're they after ya for?"

"Something I didn't do," I mutter.

He barks out a laugh, more high-pitched than I would have expected. "I hear that. Oh, I hear that all right. Damn pigs. Well, look, ya know what they say. Ya don't have to go home, but ya can't stay here."

"Sure. No problem." Not that I want to stay here, anyway. Rhonda's still looking at me like I stole her favorite chew toy. Or maybe like I *am* her favorite chew toy. "I just need... a few minutes?"

Larry laughs again, that same high-pitched giggle. "I'll say ya do, girlie. Don't think they're going anywhere."

I sneak another glance over there and see that he's right. Detectives Douglas and Vyas are at the base of the back staircase, conferring with the other two uniformed officers. All four of them look unhappy, but the detectives mostly look pissed and the unis mostly look chagrined. As I watch, one of them stretches a roll of yellow police tape across the bottom of the stairs.

Great. They're definitely not going anywhere. One of the detectives glances over at the scrapyard, and Larry throws up a one-fingered salute. I duck down behind the car again. Two seconds and my heart rate is sky-high again. How the hell am I going to get out of here?

To my surprise, it's Larry to the rescue.

"Wait here," he grumbles. "Come on, Rhonda."

He trudges back to the scrapyard's principal building, a tiny little shed that's barely more than a lean-to. Rhonda trots after him. I stay crouched in the dirt, sneaking glances back at the motel whenever it's safe to do so. The cops definitely aren't going anywhere — as I watch, more of them arrive.

They must be searching the room. I consider all the things that I left in there — fingerprints, DNA, an empty box of hair dye. Not to mention almost all the new clothes I just bought, the stuff of Enid's that Heath brought me. How long is it going to take them to piece it together? How long is it going to be before they find something that leads them straight to me?

Larry reappears and thrusts something out at me. When I take it, I realize it's a set of coveralls, identical to the ones he's wearing. The name tag on this pair says 'Gil.'

"Thank you," I whisper, tears pricking my eyes. I brush them away hastily, while Larry looks away.

Staying low to the ground, I pull on the coveralls. They're

big enough that they go on easily over my regular clothes. With my hat and sunglasses, no one would recognize me.

"Come on," Larry mutters when I'm ready. "I'll walk you to the front gate."

I rise on shaking legs and follow Larry. One of the uniformed cops, still stationed at the base of the motel stairs, glances over at us. My heart skips a beat or two, until he looks away again. I breathe out. We make our way to the front of the yard.

"Keep the coveralls," Larry says gruffly as we stand at the entrance to the next street over. "Might come in handy."

"Thank you," I say again. My throat tightens. "Hey, do you know of any motels similar to the Sunset? You know — somewhere they don't ask too many questions."

Larry considers the question for a minute, then says, "The Meadows. It's in Queens. That too far?"

Nothing is too far, I think, sneaking another look back at the Sunset Motel.

With some difficulty, I finally find The Meadows Motor Inn. My first thought is that it should have been called The Murders. The outside is dilapidated, with a crumbling plaster exterior and a front office door that's nearly falling off the hinges.

Beggars can't be choosers, I remind myself, as I let the office door swing closed behind me and step back outside. The room had cost me seventy bucks, almost all of what I had left from the money Heath gave me at Walmart.

I find the room and let myself in. As soon as I step into the dark interior, I burst out laughing.

"Oh God. Larry, you perv." The room is absolutely, one hundred percent, without a doubt, a sex room. Red sheets on the bed, black wallpaper, mirrors on the ceiling. No wonder the front desk guy had looked at me weird when I told him I was going to be the only one staying in the room.

I sit delicately on the edge of the bed, trying not to think too hard about the atrocities that have been committed here. At least the black wallpaper makes the room dim — it's hard to see if there are stains anywhere. A small blessing.

But that's about the only thing that's going my way. I don't know what to do. I could only afford to pay for one night here, and I have nothing on me — no clothes or food. Just the stuff on my back, and a wallet in my pocket that I can't really use.

I need help.

I need *Heath.*

Even though it's dangerous to call him, I don't know what other choice I have.

There's a payphone here at The Murders — sorry, The Meadows — but I'm not that stupid. If the police are tracking him, if they check his phone records, it will take them five seconds to figure out I'm staying here. I'll have to find another payphone.

I walk almost thirty blocks before I find one. I'm almost ready to give up hope when I see it, nestled next to a vending machine at a gas station. I go inside and get some change, along with a bag of chips and a cold burrito, and go back out. But when I stand in front of the phone, I realize something.

I don't know Heath's phone number.

Damn. I stare at the phone in despair for a minute before realizing what I have to do. I don't know Heath's number... but I know the Connollys' home phone number. I've been calling them since I was a kid, long before either Enid or I had cell phones. It's as ingrained in my memory as my own.

Even though I hate to involve anyone else in this saga, I pick up the phone and dial before I can change my mind. I pray Enid will answer instead of her mother, and I breathe a sigh of relief when she does.

"Enid, it's me. Alice."

"Alice!" she shrieks. "Oh my God, where are you? Are you okay? We're all worried sick about you."

"I'm fine. Mostly. But I need help."

"Anything. I'll do anything you need me to."

"Actually... can you get Heath to call me?"

She's silent for a minute. Then, "I knew he was helping you."

"Don't be mad at him. I don't know what I would have done without him."

"I'm not mad at him. I just can't understand why you didn't come to me. You know I'd do anything for you."

"I know. I love you for it. But this is such a mess. I don't want to drag anyone else in. Can you just get Heath to call me? Right away?" I give her the number of the payphone.

"Fine. Can't you at least tell me where you are? If you're safe?"

"I can't tell you where I am. But yes, I'm safe." Safe enough, anyway. I still have no idea how the cops found out I was at the Sunset Motel, so I don't know how easy it will be for them to find me at The Meadows.

I get Enid off the phone and wait. And wait some more.

Finally, the phone rings.

"Alice?" I breathe a sigh of relief at the sound of Heath's voice. "Thank God. What's going on? Are you okay? Did something happen at The Grant?"

"I never made it to The Grant. The cops showed up at the motel."

"Shit. Are you okay? They let you go?"

"They didn't find me. I snuck out the back and over the fence."

He's silent for a moment. "I don't like this. You shouldn't be alone. It's too dangerous. Where are you?"

"At a gas station in Queens. I found another place to stay for now, but I don't know." I fight the tightening in my throat, the tears that threaten to spill over. I'm so damn tired of being scared all the time.

"I'm coming to you now. Tell me where to find you." His tone brooks no argument. So, for once, I don't argue.

I walk back to The Meadows, and Heath arrives about twenty minutes later. I'm so relieved to see him that I collapse against his chest. He wraps me in a tight hug, which lasts all of about thirty seconds before I pull away, mortified.

"Sorry," I mutter. "I'm fine."

"Don't worry about it. Want to explain the coveralls?"

I laugh. I'd almost forgotten I was wearing them. "Never

underestimate the kindness of strangers," I say. "Or old guys who hate cops."

"I'll take your word on that."

I sit down on the bed. Now that my partner in crime is here, I'm eager to hash out my thoughts with him. "How do you think they knew I was there? Do you think that peeled grape in the front office called them?"

Heath sighs and sits down on the bed. If he finds the erotic decor off-putting, he hasn't said so. Instead of answering me, he takes out his phone and scrolls for a minute. Finally, he looks up. "I have to show you something," he says. "And you're not going to like it."

THIRTY-NINE

I STARE DOWN at the screen of Heath's phone. Blaring up at me is my picture, the same one from my security badge at The Grant, the same one they've plastered all over the news for the past few days. "Yeah, so?"

"Here. Look."

He hands the phone to me and I scroll down. I gasp.

"Chambers Family Offers $250,000 Reward For Information In Death Of Son," I read. "Shit."

"Yeah," Heath agrees.

I keep reading.

"The family of slain developer Weston Chambers has today announced a reward of $250,000 for anyone able to provide credible information that leads to the capture of their son's killer, or to the location of Alice Brewster, a person of interest in the case."

"I guess we know why the police were at the Sunset Motel," he says grimly.

"That bastard turned me in, didn't he?" Damn you, you peeled grape.

"That'd be my guess. You checked in before you changed your hair. He probably recognized you when he saw your picture. It's all over the news."

I flop down on the bed beside him. "This is…"

"Terrible?" he offers.

"Yeah. I'm screwed."

"It's certainly going to make things more difficult," he agrees.

"I can't go to The Grant now. Too many people there know me. Someone will recognize me, even with the hair and the clothes. They'll turn me in."

"What about your friend? Minnie? Would she turn you in?"

I consider this. "I'd like to think she wouldn't, but I don't know. I know her family could use the money, and I wouldn't exactly blame her if she did. Two hundred and fifty grand is a lot. For anyone."

"What if I went? Maybe I could find out if Sam worked there."

"How would you do that? It's not like at the cupcake place, where we could talk them into giving us information. The Grant has a whole HR department and a boatload of lawyers. They're not going to give out information like that to just anyone. I thought I could get Minnie to help — she knows almost everyone who's ever worked there."

"Maybe I could talk to her. Describe her, and I'll find her."

"I don't know. For now, we're in a good position — no one

knows you're helping me. If you start asking around at The Grant, it won't take long for someone to put two and two together."

"Well, what else are we going to do?"

But my mind is still hanging out on something from a few seconds ago. It nags at my consciousness.

Then it hits me. *Frosting Queen.* "What if we went back to Lola Hardwick?"

"What good would that do? She already said she doesn't know Taylor."

"She doesn't know Taylor — but she might know Samantha Dennings."

"You're right." Heath's face perks up, but just as quickly, he frowns. "Do you think it's too risky?"

"It's risky, yes. But hopefully she won't recognize me. There's no reason for her to think I have anything to do with this news story. I'm just a random person looking for another random person. There's nothing to connect me or Sam to Weston Chambers, at least not as far as Lola's concerned."

"Okay, okay. I'll trust your judgement on this one."

"You don't think it's a good idea?"

"I think we have to do something," he says with a sigh. "So let's go. But maybe leave the coveralls on."

Once again, we park Heath's car at a car park near the subway and take the train into Manhattan. We go straight to the Times Square location. It's as busy as last time, and the crowd fills me with dread. Is that guy staring at me? That mom who just turned around, did she recognize me? Is she secretly photographing me with her phone right now?

At the counter, there are three young women working, none of whom were here last time. I decide to bypass the royal security brigade and head straight for the door that leads to the back.

A blonde in a tiara and pink ballgown spies us from over the counter. "I'm sorry, no guests beyond the moat!" she singsongs.

"We're here to see Lola Hardwick," I say, not looking up. "She's expecting us."

"I'll just confirm that with her," she chirps, rushing around the counter. Her name tag says Queen Inga.

"There's no need to confirm." I push past her, opening the back door.

"You can't go back there," she shouts, her lilting voice transforming to something much harsher and with a slight Scandinavian accent.

"We'll only be a minute," I promise as the door swings closed behind us. A minute later, Queen Inga charges in after us. We go straight for the door of Lola's office.

When we bust in, she looks up in surprise. It's the most expression I've ever seen on her face.

"Remember us?" I smile.

Queen Inga bursts in right after. "I'm sorry, Lola. They just charged in. Do you want me to call the police?"

"No. Thanks, Inga. We don't need the police here. It's bad for business," she says, eyeing me so that I know it's not out of any concern for me that she's holding off on calling them. "You can go." She dismisses Inga.

Inga casts one last glare our way and storms back to the front of the shop.

"You're back," Lola observes.

"I have another name for you," I say.

"Another one? How many people are you looking for? And why did they all work here?"

"Not multiple people," I say. "Just one. Samantha Dennings."

Lola's face twists, almost imperceptibly, and flattens back to neutral. "Why are you looking for Sam Dennings?"

"Let's just say I have some business to discuss with her."

"Well, let me pass along a piece of advice — don't do business with that woman."

"So she worked here. Do you still have her contact information? Phone number, address, emergency contact — anything at all."

Lola sits back, considering us. "Why would I give that information to you? It's private personnel info."

I consider trying to bribe her the same way I did with Paul from the Airbnb, but something tells me Lola Hardwick can't be bribed. But I wonder if I can appeal to her sense of justice?

"Sam Dennings fucked me over," I explain. "Big time. And I'm in a real jam now, thanks to her. I want to go to the police, but I need more proof first."

She considers this. Considers me. "Last time you were here you said you were looking for someone named Taylor."

"That's what she told me her name was. She told me a lot of lies, actually, but that was one of them. It's taken us three days and a four-hour road trip to figure out who she really is."

Lola grins ruefully. "I wish I could say that surprised me. We had our own problems with Samantha Dennings."

I hold my breath. I don't want to say anything to break the spell as Lola types something on her clunker of a laptop.

"I have an address for her," she says finally. "I can't guarantee she still lives there, though. Hell, I can't guarantee she *ever* lived there. Like you said, she's a brilliant liar. A thief, too."

"I'll take it," I say hastily. "Any info you have."

She looks up at me. Her brows narrow as she studies me. I'm sweating. These coveralls are too hot, and the ovens from the bakery keep this place toasty as it is. And is it me or did the air stop circulating?

"I knew you looked familiar," Lola says, her mouth curling into a grin. "And I just figured out why." She turns her laptop to show me the screen, and there I am. That damn hotel photo again. "That's you, isn't it? You're Alice Brewster. You're the one they're looking for."

My stomach sinks down to my knees. Heath's hand is on my elbow. "Let's go," he hisses under his breath.

But I meet Lola's eye. "Maybe it is, maybe it isn't."

"Oh, it is. I have an excellent eye for faces. You've changed your hair, but the eyes, the lips, the nose — oh yeah. That's all you."

There's no point in lying. "It's me." I agree. "And I'm on the news because of Taylor. Sam Dennings. This is her scheme and somehow I'm the one who got caught in it."

"So tell me why I shouldn't call the police?"

"Because justice is better than cash," I say plainly. "You said yourself, you had your share of problems with Sam. I'm trying to make things right. And maybe making things right for me means making them right for you, too."

"You know they'll give me two hundred and fifty thousand if I turn you in, right? You think pretty highly of justice."

"I do and I think you do, too. I know what it feels like to sell your soul for some cold hard cash, and trust me, it doesn't feel good."

Lola considers this. After what feels like an eternity, she jots something down on a scrap of paper. "Fifty-seven Towers Road, Brooklyn. That's the address I have for her. Like I said, I don't know if it's any good. In thirty minutes, I'm going to call the tip line and tell them you were just here."

I snatch the paper out of her hand and nod my understanding. "Thanks for your help," I say. "I won't forget it."

"Hm," is all she says.

We rush out of the store, leaving Lola Hardwick in her dim office, deep in the heart of the pinkest building in Times Square.

We ride the subway back out to Queens. Once again, when we emerge, I'm terrified that we're going to find a SWAT unit surrounding Heath's car, but the place is as empty as when we left it. I have the same fear when we pull up into the motel parking lot, but there are no cop cars around, and the room seems undisturbed.

"You should probably go home for the night," I tell Heath

once I'm satisfied that no one has tracked me down here. "Your family and your job are going to be wondering where you are."

He frowns. "I don't like the idea of leaving you here alone."

"I'll be fine," I promise. "You've spent too much time with me already. Don't you have your own life to get back to?"

For a minute, he looks away. His gaze is drawn to the window; he yanks the curtains closed. "In a weird way, I've enjoyed this," he says while his back is to me. "Not the part where we're on the run from the law, but helping you. I've enjoyed that part."

"Me, too," I admit. "I'm grateful for your help. But I'll be fine for the night. Go home, get some sleep. Check on Enid and my mom, if you really want to do something useful. But I'm fine here by myself."

He sighs. "Okay. I guess you're right. I could use some clean clothes, anyway."

"Yeah, you could."

"Hey, I'm not the only one. You going to wear that outfit all day tomorrow, too? You smell like a gas station." He flashes me a grin and turns to go. Then he turns back. His eyes narrow. "Wait a minute. Why aren't you in a rush to go to Sam's place now that you have the address?"

"I don't know. I figured we could go in the morning."

"You're going to go over there, aren't you? That's why you want me to leave. You're going to confront her on your own."

I laugh. "As if. I'm too tired to even think about that right now. I'm going to kick back, watch some television, and sleep. In the morning, we can make a plan. We'll go over there together." As if to prove how serious I am, I flop down on the bed, grab the remote, and turn on the TV.

Heath continues to watch me suspiciously. As if, after all this, he doesn't trust me.

"Go, Heath, please. I promise I'm not going anywhere."

"Fine," he says. "But I'll be back around eight tomorrow. Don't you dare leave this hotel room between now and then. Not even to go get ice."

"Do you think I'd trust this motel's ice? There are probably severed body parts cooling in there."

"I'll see you in the morning."

I listen to him leave, his footsteps barely audible over the sound of the cheesy sitcom blaring from the television. The picture on the screen flickers, goes to snow, stabilizes again. A fat man with a far-too attractive wife shrugs comically and a studio audience guffaws. God, I hate basic cable.

As soon as I'm sure Heath is out of hearing range, I turn off the television and creep over to the window. I pull the grimy crimson curtain aside slightly, just in time to see Heath climb into his car and edge his way out of the parking lot. His taillights disappear down the adjacent road.

As soon as he's gone, I let the curtain fall closed, grab my windbreaker, and head out the door.

I'm sorry for lying to Heath, but now that I have Taylor's real address, I'm not letting her get away with this for a minute longer.

FORTY

THE APARTMENT BUILDING that Sam lives in is more rundown than the one Taylor occupied. It's in an area with a dozen other mid-rise apartment buildings, all appearing to have been built sometime in the seventies. The large sign outside the front entrance to the complex simply reads: The Estates.

Even though the weather is chilly, there are still a good number of people hanging around outside, sitting on the concrete borders of small parking lots, on the stoops of the buildings. They vary in race, in age. There are young men on one building's stoop, and a Muslim family with a handful of kids playing in the grass between two other towers. A couple of teenage girls loiter in one of the parking lots, leaning against a car and talking. From somewhere, Latin music blares. It's not the kind of place I would imagine the Taylor I knew living, but it suits what I know about Sam. She'd be invisible here, just another drop in the melting pot. I bet if I asked around, I wouldn't be able to find a single person who could even remember seeing her, let alone who knew her.

Sam's building is toward the back of the complex, where it's quieter and there are a few more trees and a few less parked cars. My heart beats faster the closer I get until, by the time I pull open the front door, it's ready to thud out of my chest. I scan the list next to the intercom. There she is — S. *Dennings*. After this long, it's hard to believe that she's real. That I've really found her. I hit the buzz code for her apartment. My hands shake.

I steel myself in anticipation of hearing her voice again, but the intercom keeps ringing. No one picks up. I hit the buzzer to dial a second time, but once again, there's no answer.

"Come on, Taylor." I scan the vestibule, wondering if this is one of those buildings with a camera that allows residents to see who's buzzing them. If Sam can see me down here, she isn't likely to let me up. But there's nothing like that. The security system is pretty low tech, just the basic intercom setup.

I can't walk away from here empty-handed, so after trying Taylor's apartment a few more times, I buzz random units. It takes me a few tries to find someone who actually picks up, so when they do, I'm momentarily startled.

"Amazon package," I eventually announce, holding my breath.

Sure enough, a second later, the front door buzzes as it unlocks. I hurry into the building and head straight up to Sam's apartment.

I bang on her door. No answer. I bang again. "Package

delivery for Sam Dennings," I say, in the gruffest voice I can muster. There's no peephole in the door, so if she's in there, I'm hoping that's enough to get her to answer.

But no dice. The door remains firmly, resolutely closed. Unlike at the last apartment building, no irritated neighbor has come out to blast me. There are definitely people home; muffled chatter comes from the closer units, and the smell of fresh garlic and a melange of spices permeates the air. I bang one more time on Sam's door before groaning in frustration. I can't believe this. I can't believe that after all I've gone through to find her, she's still somehow eluding me.

"Not forever, though," I mutter under my breath. This time I know where she lives. And she has to come home eventually. When she does, I'll be waiting.

Outside, I stand in front of her building, scouting the surrounding area in search of a spot where I can wait that won't be immediately visible to Sam when she arrives. I spy a small walking path that runs through a thicket of trees at the edge of The Estates and decide that should work. The shadows of the trees will camouflage my position, but allow me an unobstructed view of the front of Taylor's building.

I'm about to walk off the path when suddenly a hand squeezes around my upper arm.

The voice that accosts me is a low hiss. Angry. "What the hell are you doing here?"

FORTY-ONE

I FREEZE, my heart pounding out a terrified tattoo in my chest. "Heath! You scared the shit out of me. What are you doing here?"

"You promised me, Alice. You promised me you were going to stay at the motel for the night."

"I couldn't." I won't bother apologizing. He wouldn't believe me, anyway. "I had to see her, Heath. I had to try. I need answers. You don't understand how this feels."

He harrumphs something under his breath.

"Anyway," I prod, yanking my arm out of his grip. " I thought you were going home."

"I was about to, but I couldn't get the thought out of my head that you were going to try something stupid. I went back to the motel and found you gone. Somehow, I just knew I'd find you here." He looks at me pointedly, but I shrug.

"You caught me," I say. "But it doesn't matter, because she's not home. There's no answer at her apartment. I even went in and knocked on the door. Nothing."

Heath sighs. He glances around the complex, but there's no one around, or at least not anyone who's paying any attention to us. "Come on," he says through gritted teeth.

He drags me back to the vestibule of Sam's building. He finds her name on the directory, just like I did, and tries dialing it, just like I did.

I hold my breath, hoping that somehow he'll have better luck than I did, but again there's no answer.

Heath dials random numbers, just like I did, and when one finally picks up, he says, "Delivery from Amazon." The door buzzes open without question.

"That's exactly how I got in," I say, biting back my first laugh in what feels like years.

"People are predictable."

We go up to the eighth floor, down the silent hallway to Sam's apartment. Heath knocks. There's no answer.

"Never speak of this again," Heath says, pulling out his credit card. He slips it between the door and the jamb and wiggles it. "We're lucky this door hardware probably hasn't been updated since they built the place."

"Where the hell did you learn that?"

He glares up at me.

"Oh, right, we're not speaking of it." I hold my tongue and thank my lucky stars when the door pops open. We're actually doing this — breaking into Sam's apartment. I wish I could say I feel guilty, but I don't. Not in the least.

Heath ushers me in and closes the door quickly behind us. The space is dark. I go to flip on the light switch, but his hand covers mine.

"Don't," he says. "Let's figure out which windows are

visible from the entrance, first. In case she comes home. If she sees a light on, she might know something's up."

He picks his way through the outlined shapes of a sofa and an armchair, past a coffee table and a standing lamp, over to the rather large window that takes up a third of the wall space. He peers out.

"Okay, we're in luck. Her unit faces the rear of the building."

"So I can turn on the light?"

"Let's try this." He flicks on the lamp near the end of the sofa. It's not overly bright, but it casts enough illumination that we can see.

And what we see is not good.

The apartment is almost empty. Basic furniture still stands — the sofa, the coffee table, a dining room table. But there's absolutely nothing personal in the room. The bookshelf across from the sofa is empty, though the dust on the shelves shows that until recently, they were stacked with books and random objects. There are no pictures on the wall, but the slight fading of the paint indicates where they used to hang.

"No, no, no," I mutter under my breath. I move through the apartment. In the kitchen, I find one of the cabinet doors open. The cabinet itself is almost empty, and a cardboard box sits on the countertop, stacked with random mugs and glassware wrapped in newspaper. On the side of the box, someone — presumably Sam — has written the word 'donate.' Next to the box is a black Sharpie and a roll of packing tape.

"I don't believe this. She's leaving."

"Let's not panic," Heath says. "Maybe she's just doing some spring cleaning."

I shake my head. I already know. She's done whatever it was she came here to do, and now she's running. And why wouldn't she? She's got the money to go anywhere, and she has to know that if she stayed here, there's a possibility that I'd eventually be able to track her down.

I open all the other cabinets in the kitchen. Almost all of them are empty. I find only the most random assortment of items — a cracked plate, a rusty cheese grater, a wooden spoon, blackened on the end. The fridge is equally barren. The only things in there are a quarter of a jar of fake parmesan cheese and a box of baking soda.

"God dammit!" I can't keep my voice low. She's about to slip from between my fingers. All this work to find her and she's going to get away.

"Calm down," Heath says. "Let's see if we can figure this out. She could be moving apartments. It happens, you know."

I grudgingly set about exploring the rest of the apartment. The bathroom hasn't been so thoroughly picked over yet. Beside the sink sits a pink plastic bin of makeup — eye shadows in every color of the rainbow, more lipsticks than Sephora, six different types of mascara. In the medicine chest, I find even more products: lotions, potions, face masks, hair masks, and, perhaps most unexpectedly, an obscene amount of heartburn medication. Under the sink, I find a hair dryer, curling wand, and straightening iron.

This room, this collection of things, is the one area that truly feels like the Taylor I knew. This is the glamorous party girl I thought I was befriending.

I slam the cabinet closed in frustration. It's not getting me any closer to finding her, or figuring out where she's going.

"Uh, Alice?" Heath's voice echoes from another room.

I emerge to find him in the bedroom. Like the living room, Sam has emptied it of almost everything personal. The closet is empty, and most of the clothes appear to have already been donated or trashed. There's one small garbage bag shoved full of sweaters and in the corner sits a suitcase, neatly packed.

I kneel in front of it, rifling through the shirts and dresses. The motion of my hands through the fabric rustles up a sweet floral smell that immediately reminds me of Taylor. These are definitely her clothes. And probably the ones she wears most often. The ones she'd want to take with her if she was running.

I look up at Heath. He's standing in front of a desk where there's a laptop and a small sheaf of papers. He holds one of the pages up and waves it at me.

"You were right."

I jump up and snatch the sheet out of his hand. I scan the contents, my stomach clenching as understanding sinks in. It's a flight itinerary.

"She's going to California," I whisper.

"In three days."

"Dammit." She'd always talked about California, I remember. In fact, I'd even offered to help pay her way. I want to smack my former self. How she must have laughed at me. How stupid she must have thought I was. How naïve.

"What do you want to do?" Heath asks.

"I don't know." For the first time, I'm truly stumped. I

don't know what I'd been hoping to find here — evidence that Taylor had set me up for Weston's murder? — but I certainly hadn't expected to find that I only had three days before Sam Dennings disappeared forever.

I thrust the paper back at Heath. "Take a picture of that, okay? At least we'll have some record."

I scan the other pages on the desk. One of them is a calendar. At the top is a logo with an illustrated coffee cup, a line drawing of steam wafting off it.

"Steamers Coffee Shop," I read. "Isn't that near Columbia?"

"I think so." Heath finishes photographing Sam's flight information and sets the page back down on the desk.

"This must be where she works." I scan the calendar more closely, noting the dates at the top. "It's this week's shift schedule."

"Is she at work right now?"

I scan the page. "No. Tomorrow she works six in the morning until two. Friday she's working from three until ten at night."

"She leaves Saturday."

"So Friday's her last shift." I thrust the page out. "Take a picture of this one, too, please."

"What are you thinking?"

"I don't know yet, but it's good to know her schedule for the rest of the week, don't you think?"

He agrees and snaps the photo, before putting all the pages together on the desk again.

"Since she's not working right now, we don't know when

she's going to be home," he points out. "So maybe we should get out of here before she shows up and catches us."

I reluctantly agree, even though a part of me would love to have her walk in and catch us. At least I'd finally have the chance to confront her.

Instead, I follow Heath out into the living room, where we switch off the lamp and exit the apartment.

FORTY-TWO

IN THE MORNING, I expect Heath to arrive bright and early, but by ten o'clock, there's no sign of him. I try to keep myself occupied in the motel room, watching mindless morning talk shows and eating Snickers bars from the motel vending machine. By noon, he still hasn't appeared. I've given up on the television and pace back and forth across the dingy carpet of my room, counting the cigarette burns on the floor and the water stains on the ceiling, just to occupy my mind.

There's a small, dodgy coffee shop right across the road from the motel, so around lunch time I risk a quick visit to pick up some java and a toasted bagel with my last few dollars, before hurtling back to the sanctity of The Meadows. I don't know if I'm doing it because I really need the coffee, or because I really need to get out of that room, if even for a few minutes.

Back inside, I resume my pacing. Where the hell is Heath? Is he mad at me for sneaking off to Sam's last night? No. Even if he is, it wouldn't be like him to punish me like this. More likely, something's preventing him from making it back out here. Are the police at his house? Are they at mine? Maybe he suspects they're tailing him and he doesn't want to risk leading them back here.

As the hours tick by, my thoughts darken. How do I know I can trust Heath? I mean, really? Yes, he's helped me out these last few days — but why? What's in this for him? And isn't there more in it for him if he turns me in? Two hundred and fifty thousand dollars — that would go a long way toward the house he wants to buy someday, to helping his family.

I curse myself for not picking up a prepaid cell phone. At least then I could call him. I debate walking to the gas station payphone again, but what if he shows up while I'm gone? He'll worry if I'm not here.

If he's even planning to come. If he hasn't told the police exactly where I am already.

I stand paralyzed at the window of my room, peeking out the curtains every few minutes, hoping to see Heath's car pull up, but terrified that I'm going to find a police cruiser instead.

Finally, just before four o'clock, there's a knock on the door.

"It's me," Heath says. I let him in and he closes the door and locks it behind him. "Sorry it took me so long."

I'm so relieved to see him that I throw my arms around him. Tears sting my eyes. "What happened? Are you okay? Is everyone else okay?"

"I'm fine." He hesitates for a second, but returns the hug.

Somehow, we shuffle over to the bed and sit down, still close. I wipe my eyes, hoping he won't see. I'm embarrassed by my outburst, so I thrust out the paper bag I'd picked up earlier. "I got you a donut."

"You went out again?" His brows narrow.

"Just to the coffee shop across the street. No one saw me."

"You can't take risks like that, Alice." He appears satisfied that I'm suitably chagrined because he takes the chocolate glazed out of the bag. "But thank you."

"So what took you so long, anyway?"

He takes a bite of the donut, chewing slowly. I get the sense that he's buying time.

My stomach tightens. I can't take anything else. "Tell me."

When he finally swallows, he says, "Things aren't going that great for your mom."

"No." My hand flies to my mouth.

"She's fine," he says hastily. "Physically. But the media figured out who she is, that she's your mother. They're camped outside your house."

"Oh no." Guilt swims in my stomach. She already freezes up every time the phone rings, at every knock on the door. I can't imagine how she's dealing with this sudden bombardment of attention. "Can't the police make them leave? She has nothing to do with this."

"Enid called them already. Apparently, no one's actually breaking the law. As long as they stay on the sidewalk."

"But I'm the one they want, not her."

He shrugs, taking another huge bite of the donut. "But you're not there. And besides, you know what people are like. They're as interested in the woman who raised a murderer as they are in the murderer herself."

I shoot him a glare, and he holds up one hand innocently. "Not that you're a murderer, of course. But, you know. From their perspective."

I slump backward, any mounting anger already deflated. There's nothing I can do to help her; the best option is to clear my name. Then and only then will they go away.

I hope.

Heath finishes the donut and licks his fingers. "Anyway, I had the idea to go over to your house to check in on her because I wanted to let her know you were okay. But Enid went over this morning, and I didn't want to say anything in front of her, and then my mom went over around lunch time. By the time I could get over there on my own, it was almost two o'clock. That's why it took me so long to get here."

"Wait, so you actually talked to her?"

He nods his affirmation. "She's holding up well. Better than you're probably thinking. Mostly, she's worried about you. I let her know you're surviving, that you're just trying to get the proof you need to provide the police."

"So she knows I'm innocent?"

Heath rolls his eyes. "Alice, she didn't need me to tell her that. She knows you didn't do this. I only went to make sure she knew you were safe, that you had at least one person looking out for you."

I have an almost irresistible urge to hug him again. Instead, I lean against his shoulder. "Thank you for that. How's Enid?"

"She's good. She's checking in on your mom a lot. Now that she knows for sure that I've been helping you, she keeps making these cryptic comments about me being a white knight. And she noticed that her green jacket was missing."

"Shit. She's not getting it back, either. It's lost to the Sunset Motel. Tell her I'll buy her a new one if I ever get out of this mess."

"Not *if*," Heath says. "*When.*"

"I'm not too optimistic about that. What else did Enid say? Is she upset that you're helping me? She knows to keep her mouth shut, right?" I hate the thought of forcing Enid to lie to the police, but that's the world I'm living in.

"God, no. If anything, she's pissed that I'm the one helping you and not her."

I smile at that and make a silent vow to myself to never take Enid for granted again. I'm lucky to have such a good friend. Two good friends, actually. Though, at the moment, I don't know whether Heath is my friend or something else. But that's a concern for another time.

"Have you given any more thought to what you want to do?" he says, balling up the bag from the donut and tossing it in the nearby trash.

Have I? Only the entire night. I laid awake for hours thinking about how I can make this right. What I really need is proof that I didn't kill Weston, that Sam set me up. But I haven't been able to come up with a single piece of evidence that would ultimately prove she's the guilty one. Not when she's done such an excellent job setting me up to take the fall.

No, I need her to confess and I need to record her doing it. That's the only thing that'll make me feel truly confident about going to the police. If I have a video of Sam admitting that she set me up, I can go to them with my story. And if that's not enough, I can send the tape to the media. They'd be all over a story like that. If the media can make my mother's life miserable, they can make Sam's life miserable, too.

There's still a chance that things might not go my way, but the way I see it, this is the only option I have left.

"We need to break into her apartment again," I tell Heath.

"But we've already been in her apartment. We didn't find anything to prove your innocence."

"We're not looking for a thing. We're looking for *her*." I smile grimly. "We can do it tomorrow night. She's working until ten p.m., and since her flight is the next afternoon, she'll almost certainly come straight home after work to finish up any last-minute packing. When she gets there, I'm going to be waiting for her."

"We're going to confront her? Just like that?"

"Not we — *me*. It's the only way. I need her to confess."

He shakes his head. "No way. I'm not letting you be alone with that psycho. She's already killed one person. What's to say she won't do the same thing to you when she finds out you know who she really is?"

"You can be there," I allow. "But I want you out of sight. You can hide in the bathroom or something. I need her to think it's just the two of us. Her and me. I'll even let her search me to prove I'm not using my phone to try to trap her. Meanwhile, you can be recording the whole thing. And you'll be able to step in if things get out of hand."

"Step in? What if she has a gun? I'm all for being the hero here, but I'm not exactly bulletproof."

"She won't have a gun. That's not her style."

"Oh, good, so she'll just be stabbing you."

I roll my eyes. "She's not going to stab me. Think about it. She set me up because she wanted Weston dead and she didn't want to take the fall for it. If she kills me, her story goes up in smoke."

Heath scrubs a hand over his jaw. The stubble makes a rough scratching sound. "Alice, I don't know about this."

"Do you have any better ideas?"

He's silent, and I know he doesn't. I've thought through every possible scenario. The only way to prove that Sam killed Weston is to get her to admit it.

But, if I'm being honest, I want this for me, too. I want to hear her say it and I want to see her face when she does. It's the only way I'll be able to reconcile the two women in my mind — Taylor and Sam. If I don't do this, I'll always wonder which was the real one. And why I'm the one who got trapped in her web.

Heath and I go over the details of the plan over and over, working out the best time to get to Sam's apartment, and where Heath can get the best angle for recording, and how to push her toward answering my questions. I agree to let him call the police if things get out of hand, but I make him promise that he'll wait until we have her confession before we jump to that. The more we talk, the more excited I get and the more concerned Heath becomes.

"I hope you know what you're doing," he says when we've finalized things.

"I do," I promise. I refuse to let any of my niggling doubts, or his, bring me down. Tomorrow, I'll finally be able to confront the woman who twisted my life into something unrecognizable. It's my turn to twist it back.

"I guess I should go." Heath stands, stretches his long frame. It's past nine, and dark, and the room is chilly. "You should get some sleep. Tomorrow's going to be a long day."

The thought of him leaving pierces me in a way I'm unprepared for. "Or you could stay for a bit," I offer.

"Stay?"

"We could watch TV."

He glances from the television to me, on the bed. "Okay." He sinks back down beside me. I curl up beside him and let my head rest on his shoulder.

Heath stays for hours. We never turn on the television.

FORTY-THREE

HEATH DOESN'T STAY the night. He leaves after midnight, promising to return the next day by five. I ask him to check on my mother again, and he says he will.

I expect to fall sound asleep as soon as he's gone, but I'm awake most of the night. I fluctuate between feeling eager to confront Sam tomorrow to dreading what will happen when I see Taylor again. But most of all, I can't shake the sense that this nightmare is still far from over. I try to reassure myself that our plan will work, but inchworms of doubt still wriggle their way in. There are so many things that could go wrong.

When the sun rises, creeping in through the slit in the curtains, I'm still awake. I get up, shower in the mildewy bathroom, and sneak out for another bagel, rushing furtively back to the motel. I lie back down on the bed. That's when I finally get a couple of hours of sleep.

I'm awakened by a knock on the motel room door. I startle out of slumber and bolt from the bed. I quickly glance at the time — only three o'clock. I'm not expecting Heath for another two hours. Is he early? Or is it someone else banging on my door?

I hold my breath, waiting for Heath to announce himself. He doesn't. I'm afraid to peek through the curtains in case whoever's at the door notices even that slight movement. I stay absolutely still, praying they'll go away.

Instead, another knock comes.

"Anybody in there? NYPD. Open up if you're in there."

No. No, no, no. Not now. Not when I'm so close. What do I do? If I don't open the door, are they going to batter it open? But maybe they're not looking for me. Maybe this is something else entirely and they've knocked on my door by chance.

But even as I think it, I know the odds of that are nil. I'm not a gambling woman, but even if I was, I wouldn't bet on that. If the cops are here, they're here for me. The only question is whether they actually know I'm in here or not. Has someone tipped them off again? Or are they just searching random motels?

I decide to take my chances. If they break the door down and find me, then good for them, but I'm not going to surrender myself by opening the door and holding out my wrists for them to slap on a pair of handcuffs.

I stay stock still on the other side of the door, listening with every fiber of my being for any sign that they might be preparing to come in. There's some muttering from outside — there are definitely two officers out there — followed by what sounds like the shuffle of footsteps. A few seconds later there's another knock, but this one's slightly quieter. They're knocking on the door of the room next to mine.

I let out a ragged breath. This is good. That means they don't know I'm here. They're probably checking random motel rooms. But how did they know to come to The Meadows? The coincidence is too strong — they found me at the Sunset Motel, and again here. Unless they've got hundreds of officers out checking every motel in the five boroughs, it's unlikely that they've stumbled on me twice.

I listen through the door as they make their way down the motel's exterior corridor. Very few people seem to be in, and they clear most of the rooms quickly. As they get farther down the building, I pace the room like a caged animal, nervous and strung out. I want to wash my face, but I'm scared to run the faucet in case they hear it. I twist open a bottle of water I'd picked up from the coffee shop this morning and splash a little of that on my face instead.

After an hour has passed, I risk a glance out the window. The police cruiser's still parked in the lot, but there's no sign of the two officers. I finally let myself breathe. I leave the curtain open a slit, so I can keep an eye out without attracting any attention. I sit on the edge of the bed and watch for Heath.

A half hour later, his car pulls up in front of the room. I let out a sigh of relief. I automatically feel safer now that he's here. But as he steps out of the car, the two officers magically appear in front of him.

Shit.

"Sir," one of them says. "NYPD. Is this your room?"

"Uh, yeah," Heath answers.

"Are you staying in it alone?"

"Yes, sir."

"Do you know this woman?"

I know they're showing him a picture of me.

"No, sir," Heath lies.

"You've never seen her before? She may have darker hair."

"No, sir. Who is she?"

"Someone we're looking for. If you do see her, please call us immediately."

He hands something to Heath, who takes it and looks at it for a long while. He seems to be waiting for the officers to leave, and I remember he doesn't have a key to the room. I've got the only one. But if he knocks on the door, it'll be obvious he's not staying here alone.

I creep over to the door and twist the lock open as quietly as I can. The officers have their backs to him, conferring between themselves. I push the curtain aside slightly and wave Heath in.

He twists the knob and slips inside, closing the door quickly behind him. "Jesus. That was close." He throws a business card down on the TV stand.

"I don't understand. Do they know I'm here?"

"I don't think so. They weren't that pushy with me."

"Then what are they doing here?"

"My guess is they're canvassing as many motels as they can. They probably expect you to be in one of them, especially since they found you at the Sunset Motel. They missed you there, and they don't want to let you get away again."

"But... really? How much manpower would that take, to check every motel in New York?"

"This is the Chambers family we're talking about. Manpower is not an issue. The cops are probably shitting themselves over the fact that they haven't been able to bring you in yet. You're kind of a badass, Alice Brewster," he says with a wry smile. "A cop-evading, fugitive badass."

"Yeah, well, I don't feel very badass." The truth is, I'm terrified. Thinking about half of New York City's police department out hunting for me is enough to make me want to run and never look back.

"Hey," Heath says. He squeezes my hand. "We're almost at the end, right?"

"Right," I say, but all the doubts I had last night come racing back. What if we can't get Sam to confess? What if it's not enough?

But it *has* to be enough. Because running isn't an option. Not for me. Not anymore.

"Let's do this," I say through gritted teeth. I slide my knife into my pocket. I tell myself it's for luck, because I don't want to admit that I'm terrified I might need to use it.

By the time we're ready to leave, the police cruiser has left The Meadows parking lot. Still, we slink quietly out to the Camry, and once we're in, I slouch down low in my seat, hoping I won't be visible. If the cops talked to Heath and showed him my picture, they probably did that with everyone, which means even more people are looking for me.

But we're able to leave The Meadows without incident. We take all of my things with us, even the trash; one way or another, we won't be coming back here.

We're both silent on the drive over to The Estates. Heath parks as close as he can to the complex, and we walk to Sam's building. We get in using the same Amazon delivery line as last time and ride the elevator to Sam's apartment.

Heath pulls out his credit card right away, but I put a hand on his wrist. "Let's make sure she's not home first." Even though she's supposed to be at work, there's no guarantee she didn't change her shift.

I rap on the door and listen for any sound from inside. There's none, but something about the sound of the knock strikes me. I knock again, turning to Heath.

"Does that sound weird to you?"

"What?"

"The knock. It sounds hollow." I knock a third time to demonstrate.

"Maybe."

Dread fills me. On instinct, I reach out and twist the knob. It turns easily under my hand.

"It's unlocked," I say needlessly. I hesitate before pushing the door all the way open.

"Do you really want to do this?" Heath asks.

Instead of answering, I open the door.

The apartment is completely empty. Not in the process of being packed up like last time. Completely empty. The sofa, coffee table, and bookshelf are all gone. There isn't even a single dust bunny to show where they sat. I step fully into the apartment, hurrying through the kitchen and bedroom. It's all empty. Every single speck of Sam is gone, wiped clean.

"We're too late," I breathe. "She's already gone."

FORTY-FOUR

HEATH SPINS around in the apartment, disbelieving. "But how? She wasn't supposed to leave until tomorrow."

I shake my head. I don't know. I go into the bathroom, praying that she left behind a toothbrush, a hairbrush, something with her DNA. I know she won't have been that stupid, though. But still, I hope to find something, anything, that provides a link to Taylor. A tube of blush pink lipstick, a stray earring. A damn roll of Tums.

But there's nothing. I know that without even opening the medicine cabinet, or the cabinet beneath the sink. Because there's only one single thing in the bathroom — a note.

It's taped to the mirror of the cabinet above the sink, right at eye level. Where there's no chance I'd miss it. I rip it off and read.

Dear Alice,

You've been a more worthy foe than I anticipated. I must admit, I never expected you to find my actual apartment. How did you, by the way? I underestimated you in so many ways, it seems.

Thanks to your most thorough investigation, I've been forced to move my plans up. I won't be back to this apartment. By the time you read this, I'll already be in California.

(Or will I? There are so many places you can go from the west coast — south to Mexico, north to Canada. I dare you to try to find me.)

I enjoyed our time together, but not as much as I'm going to enjoy watching you rot in prison for the rest of your life.

All the best,

Taylor

With shaking hands, I pass the note to Heath, who's appeared behind me.

"Damn," he says when he's finished reading. "But how did she know?"

That's exactly what I'm trying to figure out. She must have known we were here last time, but how? The only two people who knew what we did are me and Heath.

Heath.

I stare into the bathroom mirror, at the reflection of the man standing behind me. He's still staring down at the note. His face is tight with worry and concern.

But is it real?

Somehow, Sam knew I had been here. Or at least, that I was planning on coming here tonight.

Somehow, the cops knew to find me at the Sunset Motel. I only narrowly escaped.

Somehow, the cops followed me to The Meadows.

Who else knew where I was? Who besides me... and Heath?

My stomach contracts. Is it possible? It can't be.

But what if it is?

I swallow. Heath looks up from the letter and catches my eye in the mirror. "I'm so sorry, Alice. What do you want to do now?"

My throat feels tight; too tight to speak. But I force the words out. "Let's go back to The Meadows. We need to regroup."

"Sure."

I walk on wooden legs toward the door. My mind races the entire time. Heath. It had seemed like a gift from the gods when his Camry pulled up beside me the night that I ran from the cops. A coincidence of gigantic — and wondrous — proportions.

But what if it wasn't a coincidence at all? What if he watched it all play out? He could easily see our backyard from the rear windows at the Connollys' house. He could have heard the cops pull up, then witnessed my escape.

I follow him out of the apartment and into the tiny elevator. Even though it's only eight floors down, the seconds crawl by. The walls narrow until I can't breathe. Heath's body looms beside me, his heat raising the temperature in this tiny prison.

When the doors finally judder open on the ground floor, I burst out of the elevator as if escaping a burning building.

"Are you okay?" Heath frowns at me.

"I'm fine. I just can't believe this is happening."

"Come on. We'll go back to the motel and think this through. We'll figure something out. I promise."

But even as we cross through the lot of The Estates, I know I can't go back to the motel with him. I can't risk it. I want to trust Heath, but it's too weird that Taylor knew I was coming tonight.

It sounds crazy, even in my own mind. Heath and Taylor don't know each other.

Or do they? Something niggles at the edge of my consciousness. A night that I spent hanging out with Enid. A Tuesday. I asked where Heath was and she said he was on a date.

A few days later, I talked to Taylor. She was full of energy. She talked about her audition for the sexual harassment video, but she said something else. *"I had a date on Tuesday."*

What if...

Oh God. My stomach twists so hard that I think I'm going to throw up. I force myself to keep putting one foot in front of the other, but all I can think of is Heath's solid presence beside me. How comforting I'd found that presence over the last few days. And how now the thought of all that time spent together sends a chill down my spine.

Has he been aligned with Taylor all this time? But why?

But the reasons don't matter right now. What matters is that I know. And knowledge is all I have to cling to. Knowledge, and the truth.

As we get closer to the street, I formulate a plan. I can't

get into that car with him. Once I do, I'll be stuck with him all the way to The Meadows. My best bet is to run. There's a subway station half a block away — I'd arrived there the first time I scoped out Taylor's apartment on my own.

We get to the Camry and I take my time at the passenger side door, pretending to tie my shoe. I wait until Heath is inside the car, until he's closed the door behind him.

Then I run.

FORTY-FIVE

IT TAKES Heath a few seconds to realize I haven't climbed into the car beside him, which buys me a bit of precious time.

"Alice!" he yells. "What are you doing?"

But I don't stop. I don't even risk a glance back. I'm too focused on getting to the subway. It's my best chance for getting out of here. I don't know what Heath will do if he catches up with me, but if he's in league with Taylor, I don't want to wait around to find out.

When I reach the subway, I barrel down the stairs so fast I almost fall flat on my face. I turn my ankle trying to catch myself, but even the stabbing pain doesn't slow me down.

It's not until I reach the bottom that I realize I don't have any money on me. I spent my last couple of dollars on that stupid bagel this morning. I could kick myself — food seems so irrelevant considering what I'm facing now.

But now that I'm here, I have no choice. Heath had to know I was heading for the subway. He can't be more than a hundred paces behind me.

The train pulls into the station. It's now or never. I jump the turnstile.

"Hey! Miss, you can't do that!"

I ignore the transit worker and barrel down the second set of stairs to track level. The train is already there and the doors are sliding shut. My escape window is disappearing before my eyes.

I fling myself at that scant opening and squeeze through it just in time. I fall against a woman with a stroller who shoots me a glare and pushes the unwieldy contraption deeper into the throng of people, who all glare at me in turn.

"Sorry," I say to everyone. "Sorry."

But inside, I'm breathing a sigh of relief. I made it. I'll ride this train to the next connecting station, then get out and switch trains. Maybe I'll do that a couple of times. Just to make sure Heath can't follow me.

But my elation quickly deescalates. Now that I've gotten away from Heath, where do I go? What do I do? I have no money, and no one else to turn to.

Except that's not true. There's always someone I can count on. Someone who would do absolutely anything for me.

My mother.

I want to go home.

As soon as I think that, a wave of bone deep exhaustion sweeps over me. I can go home.

I know the consequences of going back there. I know the media is camped out there, that the police will be watching to see if I try to make contact. I know I'll only have a small window of time before someone figures out I'm there. And

Heath — he'll be looking for me. Hopefully, he'll think that I'm unlikely to go back home, but I know he'll check there eventually.

But I'm going to do it anyway. I want to see my mother. I want to tell her everything in person. Tell her I know what she did for me all those years ago. That I love her and that I forgive her, that she never needed my forgiveness. I don't know what it will change, or if it will change anything at all, but it feels like the right thing to do.

And when I'm done with that?

I briefly consider the idea of going to California, of trying to find Taylor. But I don't know how I'd get there, and I don't know how I'd find her even if I did. Like she said in her note, she could go anywhere from there. She could be halfway to Prague by now. Or Peru. Or Pensacola.

And even if she stayed in the Los Angeles area, she could pick a brand-new name and start all over again.

No, there's only one choice available to me. One path open to take.

I'm going to go to the police.

I'll tell them everything. From start to finish — about Weston assaulting me, meeting Taylor, this bizarre setup.

I'm not very optimistic. What seems more likely? That I've been framed through some elaborate plan by a person I've never even met before, or that I killed Weston myself and have concocted this ridiculous story to try to get out of it? But I have no other choice. I'm going to take my chances and hope I get an understanding officer, one who will hear me out. I think of the detectives who came to question me that day. They'd seemed reasonable enough. Especially Detective

Vyas. There was something calm and steady about him. Maybe he'll believe me. Maybe he'll at least look into my story. If Sam worked at The Grant, if they can prove Weston assaulted her too, that would at least lend my theory some credibility.

And if not, there's always a jury. All I need is reasonable doubt, right?

My stomach twists a little at the thought. I feel as if I'm throwing myself to the wolves.

I wish I could say that I have faith in the justice system, in the boys in blue. But I don't. I don't think most of them are malicious people who are trying to lock up innocent women or anything. But I do think that people mostly only think of themselves, and what most of them want — cops and everyone else — is ease. They want the easy answer, the easy solve, the easy win, the easy life. It's the same reason the lawyers at The Grant found it easier to pay me off than to confront what happened to me. And it's why I found it easier to take the money and run.

So, no, I'm not throwing myself to the wolves. I'm throwing myself to people, and that's a whole lot scarier.

I switch trains as soon as I can, double forward and backward a couple of times before I get on the train that will lead me back to Manhattan, where I'll eventually take the ferry back to Staten Island. To my home.

FORTY-SIX

AS SOON AS I set foot on Staten Island again, I'm overcome with a sense of rightness. I'm scared out of my mind, but I also know I'm doing the right thing. No more running.

Until I get to my street.

"Shit," I mutter as I come around the corner.

I knew there'd be some media outside of my house, but this is way more than I expected. Parked in front of our house, and for a stretch of about four houses, are a bunch of news vans. I see logos for most of the local news networks, plus a couple of national ones. Even though it's almost nine o'clock at night, they're still waiting out there, hoping for a morsel of anything they can feed to their hungry audiences. Talk about wolves.

I double back to the street behind our house. I'm going to have to climb in my usual way, via the getaway tree. If I'm lucky, they'll never even know I'm here.

No more running.

Scanning the street to make sure no one is watching, I duck through the hedges in front of the pale green house directly behind my own. It's quiet back here. Quiet and cold. The grass crunches under my feet; the temperature must have dropped below freezing.

I scale the getaway tree as easily and effortlessly as I always have. For a second it's as if I'm returning home from one of my old nightly jaunts rather than walking in to say goodbye to my mother, to tell her I love her, and to ask her to pray for me. The raspy bark under my hands is comforting and familiar, like the skin of a lover.

My heart skips a beat as I reach for the bedroom window. What if Mom locked it? But when my palms push up against it, it moves easily. Had my mother failed to notice that it wasn't locked? Or had she left it open in case I decided to return home this way?

As soon as I'm inside, I slide the window shut behind me and take a deep breath. Home. The room smells different than I remember. Slightly mustier, slightly sweeter. But everything looks the same. My bed is made, and someone has set Brandy, my old stuffed horse, on the center of the pillow. *Mom.* There's a slight indent on the quilt, which tells me she's been sitting in here. Wondering about me. Worrying about me.

I leave the bedroom. The hallway is dark, but I rely on muscle memory to feel my way to the top of the stairs. There are voices coming from downstairs. The television, I think. I start down the stairs quietly, not wanting to startle my mother.

The voices become clearer, and I realize they're not

A FRIEND LIKE THAT   333

coming from the TV. It's my mother's voice that I hear, and someone else's. Enid, maybe. Thank God for Enid.

I'm almost down the stairs when something makes my blood run cold. It's not Enid down there, after all.

"There we go," the female voice says. "Nice and tight."

I'd know that throaty lilt anywhere. It's been burned into my consciousness, the deepest parts of my memory. I shiver.

Taylor.

FORTY-SEVEN

I'M ALREADY HALFWAY down the stairs when I hear her. From the volume of Taylor's voice, I'd say they're in the kitchen.

For a second, I remain frozen in place. Then, from downstairs, I hear my mother whimper and that cracks the icy sheet of my indecision. I need to call the police.

I know I left my cell phone in my bedroom when I first ran, so I creep back up the stairs and pad silently down the hall. I scan the room for the phone, but it isn't in any of the places I'd normally leave it. Not on my nightstand, not on my desk. I yank the desk drawer open, even though I never keep it there, but there's nothing but a pad of sticky notes and a couple of dead pens and dried out highlighters. I check the charger, in case Mom thought to plug it in for me, but it's not there, either.

That's when I realize my phone isn't the only thing that's missing — so is my laptop. It normally stays right in the middle of my desk, even though I don't use it for very much.

It's a beat-up old MacBook I bought on Marketplace, mostly for formatting my small scrap of a resume. The spot on the desk where the laptop should be is empty.

The police took it. I know that's right as soon as I think it. Of course they would have seized my things. My laptop, and my phone too. I push down a sick feeling at the thought of someone going through all my emails, my browser history. There's not even anything bad on there; it's the principle of the thing.

If they've taken my cell phone, that means there are no phones upstairs. My mother doesn't own a cell phone, so the only other option in the house is the landline. The phone is hardwired into the living room, but since it's cordless, the hand unit could be anywhere. If it's in the kitchen, I'm screwed.

I creep downstairs again. I've never been so grateful for carpeted stairs. My footsteps will be almost impossible to hear from the kitchen. Unless someone wanders out into the hallway and sees me, I should be able to make it to the living room undetected.

At the bottom of the stairs, I find most of the main floor bathed in darkness. The only light comes from the kitchen, where the overhead lights illuminate a horrifying scene.

Taylor stands with her back to me. My mother sits on one of the wooden chairs from our kitchen set. The chair's been pulled away from the table, positioned so that I can see my mother in profile. Taylor's used yellow nylon rope to tie her in place. The rope cuts into my mother's floral nightgown. Her expression is grim and terrified.

I fight the urge to charge at Taylor. The only thing that

stops me is the glint of the knife in Taylor's hand. One of our kitchen knives, by the looks of it. Even from here, I can tell how sharp the blade is. How much damage it could do.

Could I disarm her myself? Overpower her? Taylor has a wiry strength and about twenty pounds over my scrawny frame. And she has madness on her side. If I miscalculate my attack at all, if I don't completely subdue her, she could hurt my mother. Or worse.

I think about throwing open the front door instead. On the street outside our house are a dozen journalists, at least half as many cameras. But is an audience enough to stop Taylor? The distance from the sidewalk to the kitchen has to be at least sixty feet. She'd have time to kill my mother before anyone could get inside.

No, the best solution is to call 911. Then I can tackle her and try to get the knife away from her before she hurts anyone. At least I might be able to distract her until the cops arrive.

To get to the entrance of the living room, I have to tiptoe down the hall toward the kitchen for about six feet. I creep along the hallway as quietly as I can, pressing myself close to the wall. The hallway is dark, which works in my favor; even so, if Taylor turns around, she'll definitely be able to see me. I have to keep that from happening. Once I'm in the living room, things will be safer. Even if she hears me, she'll have to come all the way into the living room to investigate, and that will mean she won't be hovering over my mother. I can live with that. I just need to get to the phone. *Focus on that.*

I'm almost to the living room when my mother looks up and over. I can tell by the way her brow wrinkles she sees something in the hallway. I don't know if she realizes it's me or not. I hesitate for a second. Should I keep still? Wait until she looks away? But she's still squinting into the hallway, and now she's craning her neck to see better.

Dammit, Mom. I step forward a little, so she can see me fully. I move my hand flat across my throat, trying to tell her silently to cut it out. Her face relaxes immediately. She looks almost peaceful. Serene. *Too* serene.

Taylor whips her head around. Her eyes squint into the darkness. I hold my breath, but there's no hiding, not really. It's not that dark in the hallway.

"Well, well, well," Taylor says. "Look who made it in time for the show. This is working out even better than I imagined."

I brace myself, waiting for her to career toward me. But she stays where she is. She yanks out a second kitchen chair and gestures for me to sit.

"Join us, Alice," she says.

"I don't think so."

"Oh, come on. You wouldn't want me to hurt your dear sweet mom, would you?" Taylor takes a step toward Mom and presses the blade against her cheek.

My mother's jaw clenches, but she doesn't whimper.

"You have no reason to hurt her."

"You're giving me one now," she says impatiently. "I told you to sit. So take a damn seat."

I hesitate for another second. If I sit, I lose any advantage I might have. But Taylor's growing frustrated. She runs the tip of the blade along my mother's cheek, causing her to hiss with pain. A ribbon of bright red blood appears along her pale skin.

"Okay, okay." I ease into the kitchen and perch on the chair Taylor's offered.

Taylor grabs the coil of rope on the counter — the same yellow stuff she's used on Mom. I don't recognize it, which means she probably brought it with her. For what reason? Did she come thinking she'd find me here?

Taylor winds the rope around me. She does it with one hand, keeping the knife pointed in my general direction with the other. It's a precarious position, and I consider tackling her before she can restrain me completely.

"Don't even think about it," she cautions, as if reading my mind. "Not unless you're going to kill me. Because remember, even if you get free, I still have your mom tied up. You'd have to be pretty sure you could stop me before I get to her. All it would take is one slice across the carotid and she'd bleed out in seconds. Are you that fast, Alice? Fast enough to stop me from doing that?"

I clench my hands. She's right. I can't be sure that it would work, and, if I miscalculate at all, Mom would be the one to pay the price. I stay still.

But I can do something. While Taylor winds the rope around my chest and upper arms, I take a slow, deep breath, filling my lungs to capacity and stretching my ribcage as far as it'll go. I hold the breath for as long as I can, until Taylor knots the rope behind me. She stands back to admire her work, and I let the breath out slowly, hopefully without her noticing.

"That should do," she says. She turns back to Mom as I test my bindings.

Taylor's wound the rope from a couple of inches below my shoulders to just below my elbows. I can bend my arms a little, but not a lot. But the big breath I took while she was tying me up has given me a little more wiggle room than she realizes. I test the range and realize with relief that I can still reach my fingers into the pocket of my jeans. I just need to distract her long enough to do that.

"You don't have to do this," I tell her. "You were going to get away. You were going to California."

"This will be fun," Taylor says, ignoring me. "I'm going to let you watch while I kill her."

"But why?" I don't have to fake the desperation in my voice. "She has nothing to do with this. Weston's dead, just like you wanted, and no one's even looking at you. You won. Your plan worked."

"Weston?" She finally spins around to face me. "You think this is about *Weston*?"

I flinch at the level of vitriol in her voice. "What else would it be about?"

"You stupid, stupid girl," she hisses. "This was never about Weston. Weston Chambers was a sack of shit. But he was nothing more than a means to an end. This is about you, Alice. It's always been about you."

I stare open-mouthed at Taylor. "Me? But what did I ever do to you?"

"You stole my life," she roars. "The life I was supposed to have."

FORTY-EIGHT

SAM STOOD in front of the dying woman and felt nothing. She'd wondered if, when this moment finally came, she might experience some ultimate rush of empathy or compassion. Whether a lifetime of regret might well up inside of her, bathing her in a wash of forgiveness. Whether she might fall to the side of the bed, take the dry, bony hands in hers, and whisper some last goodbye. 'I love you, Mom,' or 'I know you tried.' Something like that.

But no. She felt nothing. She didn't know if it was because she could no longer feel anything at all, or if it was because all her empathy and compassion for this woman, any love she might have once felt, had been used up over the years. She supposed it didn't matter either way. She savored the cold emptiness inside her. It felt clean. Easy.

The woman on the bed turned her head with some effort. Her eyes met Sam's.

"My baby girl," she whispered. The words were stuttered and required more movements of the jaw than there were

syllables. It was like watching a skeleton try to speak, the jaw hinge working overtime in an effort to force any sound from what remained of the lips.

Sam didn't answer. She didn't want to be here, but she needed to know when it was over. She had to see with her own eyes when Evangeline left this world for whatever came next. She hadn't set foot in this squalid apartment since the last time she'd been forced to live here, and she tried to look around as little as possible. She felt no need to relive any of the memories of her childhood home. There was nothing here for her.

"I'm sorry," her mother said, that jaw working overtime again. She tried to reach for her daughter's hand, but Sam pulled back, standing just out of reach of the bed. The hand settled on the blanket again, bony and still.

Sam looked at the clock on her phone. How long would this take? Hours? Days?

In another life, her mother would have been dying in the hospital, where at least there'd be doctors and nurses to take on some of the burden. Sam didn't even know what her mother was dying of, though she presumed it was cancer. Evangeline had been getting more and more sick for the past two years, but she'd refused to see a doctor. Said she didn't deserve care, didn't deserve to get well.

Despite everything, Sam had continued to speak to her on the phone once a month, every month. Just to make sure Evangeline was still alive. Two days ago, she'd failed to answer the phone. Sam had taken a bus from the city and found her mother unable to rise from her bed. She'd been shocked at her ghastly appearance, at the way this mystery illness had hollowed her out. She'd thought about insisting Evangeline see a doctor, but she knew there was nothing the healthcare system could do for her.

Not to mention that she didn't care enough to be saddled with any of Evangeline's medical bills.

She knew her mother must be suffering, but the icy part of her didn't care. She'd endured her fair share of suffering in this life, and she had no pity for this monstrous woman who'd been at the heart of it all.

Evangeline's face twitched. Sam realized she was attempting to smile. It was a gruesome sight.

"So... like... your... father." The words took every ounce of strength her mother possessed. Her eyes fluttered closed.

Sam's heart leaped. Her father? Her mother had always claimed to not know who her father was. Sam had never doubted that, since the number of men her mother had fucked had to be well into the thousands. Sam was the daughter of a mystery donor, another anonymous monster of the hundreds — thousands, maybe — who'd passed through here over the years.

She leaned over her mother. "My father? What do you know about my father?"

"Loved... him." Evangeline's lips parted. Her tongue attempted to coat them in saliva, but there wasn't a drop of moisture left in her body.

Sam gritted her teeth. She went to the kitchen and filled a cup with water from the sink. She hadn't touched anything in the house since she'd arrived, and the sight of the moldering dishes stacked in the sink made her gag. The entire apartment had an odor of old food, stale sweat, impending death.

She took the cup and cradled it to Evangeline's lips. Most

of the water dribbled off her mother's chin, but some made it past her lips. Her eyes turned gratefully toward Sam.

Sam pulled the cup away. "Who was my father? Tell me."

"Shoe... box," Evangeline stuttered. "Closet."

Sam rushed to the closet, throwing Evangeline's meager clothes aside in search of a shoe box. When she finally unearthed it, she laughed. The box was champagne gold, labelled Jimmy Choo. There's no way her mother had ever owned a pair of Jimmy Choos in her life.

She ripped the lid off the box. Her mother's treasures tumbled to the floor. Sam crouched, rooting through them. The miscellanies of her mother's life made her sad: a cheap necklace with a heart pendant, a child's pink hair barrette, a tiny snow globe with an even tinier Manhattan encased inside. Mixed in with these was a small stack of photographs — most of them were of her, taken during the brief periods of Evangeline's sobriety. Sam rifled through them without even a pang of longing; all she wanted was her father.

One photograph stopped her. This one was of her mother and a man she didn't recognize. No, that wasn't right. She didn't know him — but she certainly recognized him. She saw her own eyes staring back at her, deep and blue. She turned the photo over. Someone had written on the back of it. There was no name on it, only a date — the year she was born. She flipped the photo back over and scrutinized her mother's image. Yes, there it was. The slight swell of early pregnancy.

She took the photo to her mother's bedside. "This is him, isn't it? My father. Tell me his name. Tell me everything."

Evangeline spoke. It took hours, took every last ounce of her breath, her energy. Sam didn't care. She pushed her mother onward. She took notes on her phone, jotting down everything she could use to track this man down. When her mother finally passed over, Sam didn't even notice. She was already googling the stranger who should have been her father. The man she had deserved to have in her life, the man who'd abandoned them both.

FORTY-NINE

TAYLOR HUNCHES in front of me, her eyes wild. She looks nothing like the girl I met a few weeks ago, the girl who'd danced at Karnival, who'd whooped with laughter as we'd vandalized an empty warehouse. Her blonde hair clumps together in unwashed tangles. Her eyes are ghostly pale without the smear of dark makeup. She brandishes the knife in front of me, as if she's waiting for her cue to shove it deep in my gullet.

"What the hell are you talking about?" I try to keep my voice level, because the situation doesn't need further escalation. But I'm shaking all over.

"You got everything, and you never even appreciated it. You never appreciated *him*," she spits.

"Taylor — Sam. Please. I don't know what you're talking about."

"I do." My mother's voice takes me by surprise. For a second, I'd forgotten there was anyone else in the room with us. "You're Ronnie's girl, aren't you?"

Taylor whips around. *"Ronnie's girl.* That's rich. I was never Ronnie's girl. That was her." She jerks her thumb toward me.

My mind struggles to keep up. "That's what this is about? My father?"

"He was my father, too," she spits. "But our lives couldn't have been more different. You got everything," Taylor says, spinning on me. "You got a house. A childhood. You got *him.*"

Everything finally clicks into place. "Your mother... she was a prostitute."

"A whore," Taylor corrects.

"And my father..."

"Fucked her and fathered me? That's what you'd like to think, isn't it? But he loved her, my mother. He told her he wanted to marry her. But he had this other family, he had to... he couldn't be with her. It broke her."

"Taylor, I—"

"My name is Sam," she roars, pushing the knife up in my face again.

"Sam, I'm sorry," I pant. The blade is precariously close to my left eye, and Taylor — *Sam* — is unhinged enough to do it. "But what does Weston have to do with any of this?"

"Weston? Nothing. I told you that already."

"So why kill him?"

"Don't you get it? This was about making you pay. You had the life I should have had and I wanted you to know the price of that."

"So you — what? You set me up for murder?"

She shrugs. "That wasn't the original plan. At first, I just wanted you to suffer the way I had."

"What do you mean?"

"Come on. Don't be stupid. I know you went to Ithaca and talked to poor old Shannon. I called her after I saw you'd been in my apartment." She laughs, seeing my surprise. "Never knew I had a camera in there, did you? There was so much you never picked up on. Stupid girl."

I don't say anything. The longer she talks, the longer I have to figure a way out of this.

"But I admit I was stupid, too. At least once. Mentioning Ithaca. God, I couldn't believe it when I said that. It was the only mistake I made when I was with you, so I knew that had to be how you'd tracked me down. Shannon—" Sam shakes her head. "God, that woman is an insufferable gossip. I'm sure she told you all the gory details of my past."

I wrack my brain, trying to remember the things Shannon had told me. It hits me all at once, a curled fist socking me in the stomach. "Your foster father. The one who—"

"Raped me, yeah. Some people sure have a funny idea of what foster care means. That disgusting asshole used to crawl into my bed every night like it was the local pub. Do you have any idea what that's like? Being twelve years old and feeling so used and disgusting?"

"No," I say honestly. There's a small part of my heart that breaks for Sam, but I can't lose sight of the reality of my situation.

"Well, I thought Weston Chambers could give you a little taste of that."

The reality of what she's saying sinks in. "You set it up? My assault? But how?" In front of me, my mother winces.

Sam shrugs. "It was easy enough. There are quite a few

websites out there where women like to spill the tea on the despicable things men do. There was lots of chatter about Weston. Once we realized the hotel had a rule about who could clean his room, we saw how easy it would be. All I had to do was get you in his room alone. I thought it would take a few tries, but imagine how pleased I was to get it in two."

The pieces click into place. Rosa's food poisoning, Camila being called away to her son's school. "You found the schedule and made sure my cleaning partner got called away."

"Bingo," she chirps happily. "I honestly didn't know if it would work or not. I had other ideas if that one failed — pretty easy to go on Craigslist and set up an ad for a rape fantasy rendezvous, if it came to that — but I liked the idea of ruining your job for you at the same time. It was kind of brilliant, don't you think?"

"Brilliant," I echo. My stomach is sour. "So you got what you wanted. He raped me. I suffered just like you did."

Her face darkens. "You didn't, though. That was the problem. It took me a while to track you down at that grungy bar you like to hang out at, but imagine how I felt when I walked in that afternoon and saw you sitting there with a check for five hundred thousand dollars. A half a million bucks, Alice. Do you know what I got when I was raped? Not five hundred thousand dollars, that's for sure. I got chlamydia. Twelve-years-old with a case of chlamydia — how do you like that?"

"I'm sorry." I really am. There's no excuse for the things that have happened to Sam. But there's no excuse for what she's done, either. "I never wanted that money. You can keep it."

She laughs. It's a hollow, unnerving sound. "It's too late for that. And it doesn't matter that you didn't want it. You still got it, didn't you? Just like you got him. Just like you got everything."

"So you wanted to punish me further. You set me up for his murder."

She grins. "Now you're getting it. We figured being in prison might be a pretty good equivalent to what I went through. No freedom, no future. I thought we had everything set, too. We made sure you'd be in Central Park, alone, when I did it. No alibi that way. The knife I used was the one from my apartment — well, Taylor's apartment. The one you used to make a sad little salad with. It had your fingerprints all over it. It should have gone flawlessly. We just didn't count on you being so wily. Frankly, you always seemed like a total doormat."

Even as I struggle to keep up with her confession, there's one detail I come back to — she keeps using the word 'we.' She *was* working with someone else. I guess my instincts about Heath were right. But I have no time to dwell on that. I try to keep Sam focused on talking to me.

"I guess I have you to thank for that," I say. "You taught me to stand up for myself. Remember when we spray painted Weston's building?" I try to push her toward a fonder memory. Maybe, if there was even an iota of something real about our friendship, it could cut the tension a little.

But Sam rolls her eyes. "God. That. It took everything I had not to slit your throat with a shard of glass from that broken window. Or maybe just beat you to death with a pipe. You were such a pansy. *'Oh Taylor, we can't! Spray painting is illegal!'*" She makes a mock pouty face.

"Sounds exactly like me."

She cracks an actual smile. "I do a wonderful impression of you. That's why, after I kill your mother, I'm going to call the police and confess to her murder. Weston's too. As you, of course."

The reality of our predicament hits me again. Sam isn't going to keep talking forever. I have to figure out a way to get into the pocket of my jeans.

"For what it's worth, I'm sorry," I tell her. "I never knew. That my father had any other children."

"Of course you didn't."

"Do you want some pictures?"

She tenses. "What?"

"Pictures. Of my dad. *Our* dad. I just thought, you probably don't have any. We have a whole album of them if you'd like some."

"It's in the living room," my mother chimes in. "I was looking at it the other day. The big burgundy leather album. It's on the coffee table, or maybe one of the side tables."

Sam squints at us. "You just want me to leave the room so you can get away."

"Where are we going to go?" I say, lifting my hands at the wrists to show how little movement I'm capable of. "The living room is literally eight feet from here."

She considers this. She seems reluctant to leave us alone, but the temptation of pictures of my father, of the man she's constructed into some sort of lost savior, proves too much to resist. She waves the knife at us and backs out of the kitchen, then ducks into the living room.

I use the time to shove my fingers into my pocket. The rope rubs hot against the skin of my forearm, but I stretch my fingers as far as I can. They finally close around the knife. I wrestle it out and keep it palmed as Sam reappears in the hallway.

"See?" I say. "We're all still here."

She glares as she dumps the album on the kitchen table. She opens it at random and flips through a few pages. I glimpse moments of my childhood from between her fingers. My First Communion, decked out in my lacy white dress and standing between my mother and father. Our family trip to the Brooklyn Zoo, me smiling and holding up my new stuffed giraffe. A photo of Mom and Dad's wedding, where my mother still looked happy and my father still looked kind.

"I'll take this whole thing," Sam announces, slamming it closed. "Of course, I'll have to crop you out of all of them," she says to me. She sneers. "No wonder you grew up to be so soft, with that childhood. Must have been nice to have Mommy and Daddy to tuck you into bed each night."

"It wasn't like that." I lick my lips and swallow. Telling her the truth is a risk, but it might distract her long enough for me to open the knife and start sawing through my bindings. "My father wasn't who you think he was."

Sam eyes me suspiciously. "Who do I think he was?"

"I don't know," I admit. "But you seem to have the idea that I had some idyllic childhood. I didn't. My father was a drunk. He was on the road half the time, but when he wasn't, he was at the bar. And when he wasn't on the road, or at the bar, he was here and those were the worst times of all."

"You're lying," she says.

"She's not," my mother chimes in. "He wasn't a good man. He used to hit me. Broke three of my ribs. My nose. My right collarbone. My left wrist — twice. And those are just the things I went to the emergency room for."

While my mother talks, I snap open the knife. The blade isn't super sharp, but I pray it'll do the job of cutting through this nylon. I twist my hand so I can angle the blade toward the rope. I saw slowly, silently. I try to catch my mother's eye, urge her to keep talking.

"I wanted to leave him," she muses. "For years, I tried. He told me he'd kill me. I believed it, too. He would have. He had a temper. A bad one. He was like you. He thought life owed him something. That there was this karmic ledger and he'd wrongly found himself in the negative."

"Did he ever hit you?" Sam spins to face me. I quickly palm the blade. It slices the skin on my palm. I try to keep the pain from my face.

"Just once," I admit. "But it wasn't a picnic watching him beat the shit out of my mother. I was too small to stop him. So I used to hide. And as I got older, I ran. The tree outside my bedroom window, that was my getaway tree. I used to leave when the fighting got really bad. I'd climb down and walk to the waterfront. I'd sit there for hours until I knew things would have calmed down. I was a coward."

"You weren't a coward," my mother whispers. "We were both doing whatever we could."

"Shut up," Sam barks. She turns to my mother again.

"Stop spinning lies about him. If he hit you, it was because you deserved it. You weren't a good wife. A good mother. It was *my* mother he wanted to be with."

My mother's head hangs. I want to punch Sam in the face, rip that knife from her hands and pummel her, but I channel my rage into sawing at my bindings. The rope frays, one thin strand at a time.

"You're wrong," my mother says. "Nothing was ever good enough for him. He was a dangerous man, and you were better off without him."

"Better off? Better off?" Sam screams. "Nothing about my life was *better*." She's waving the knife around, and it's too close to my mother's face. But Mom's expression remains passive. "Maybe you'd be better off without one of your fingers. Let's see — which one?" She grabs my mother's hand and scrapes the blade over one knuckle after another. "Or maybe the whole hand. How much better off would you be then, do you think?"

I saw frantically. I catch my mother's eye and she blinks once. She knows what I'm doing.

She turns her gaze back to Sam, her eyes searching Sam's taut face, the grim line of her mouth. "I'm sorry for what you went through," she says. "But I'm not sorry for telling you the truth. Your father was a wicked man."

"No," Sam says, agitated. "He wasn't. My mother was awful. My father was supposed to save me."

"He couldn't save anyone. He couldn't even save himself."

At last, my blade tears through the last fiber of the nylon rope. It loosens around me.

"You're lying. You didn't appreciate him, and now he's dead and I'll never..." She grabs my mother's hand, pushes it backward at the wrist, pushes it so far that I hear bone snap. My mother screams.

"I killed him," I say, hoping to draw her attention back to me.

"What?" She spins again. Her face is crazed, her pupils dilated so far that her eyes look solid black.

"He deserved it. We could never be free as long as he was alive, so one night, when he was at the bar, I took his gun from the basement and went down to find him. I waited until he came out of the bar and I shot him. The police thought it was a mugging."

"You didn't." Her face is apoplectic.

"I did."

"You took everything from me!" She lunges toward me.

"He died like a dog in the street," I spit. "And he suffered. I made sure of it."

Sam throws herself on top of me. I'm ready for her. I drive my father's knife into her side. It goes in deeper than I expect, all the way to the hilt. I pull it out and thrust again.

Sam's mouth opens in shock. Her own knife clatters to the floor. She collapses onto my lap, her mouth opening and closing like a fish. Warm blood pools onto my thighs.

I watch as Sam takes her last breath, as the sparkle leaves Taylor's eyes forever.

FIFTY

I PUSH Sam's body down onto the floor and stand up. I move on autopilot, crossing the kitchen to untie my mother. We're both crying. I can tell because I can see the wet streaks on my mother's cheeks, and I can feel the twin trails of tears from my own eyes. But the kitchen is thick with silence. It's as if I'm at the bottom of the ocean, where the weight of the water dilutes the sound, muffles the reverberations.

No one from the street, none of the media congregated outside, has come up to the house to see what's going on. The walls of this kitchen have contained the drama, the noise. The reality of what's happened here. The *un*reality. For this moment, it is only ours.

And then... a noise at the back door. Mom and I both turn as a gentle knock shatters the silence.

Enid.

I want to shoo her away, but there are no curtains in the door's window and I can tell by her expression that she sees everything — the body, the blood, the knife.

There's a crash as Enid drops something and screams. I fling the door open and yank her inside, shushing her. I don't want to draw the attention of anyone out on the street. Not yet. Not until I figure out what to do. A broken plate lies on the back step; Enid steps on chocolate chip cookies as she staggers inside.

"I can explain everything," I say as soon as I've closed the door behind her. But a delirious laugh bubbles up. Can I? Can I really explain everything that's led us to this point?

Memories flash through my mind. Meeting Taylor that day at El Diablo. Throwing money at homeless people. Dancing at Karnival. Nearly killing that guy in the alley. Vandalizing Weston's warehouse, venting all my frustration in spray paint and whiskey.

"This is Taylor," I say finally, because that's who she'll always be to me. "And she's the one who really killed Weston Chambers."

The words clarify something inside me. Calcify it. I have to call the police. Now. Even though the entire story sounds like something concocted in a bad soap opera, I have to tell them everything.

"Where's the phone?" I ask Mom.

"In the living room," she whispers, still in a stupor. Her eyes haven't left Taylor's body, the pool of blood on the black and white linoleum.

"What are you doing?" Enid asks as I leave the kitchen.

"Calling the police."

"Wait!"

I stop. "What?"

"I... think about this, Alice." Her face is a mask of panic.

"They already think you killed Weston Chambers. Now you've got another dead body in your kitchen. How is that going to look?"

I set my mouth in a grim line. It's not like I haven't considered all of that. But I'm out of options. "I have to do this."

"But just... wait." Enid's voice rises.

I grab the cordless phone from the living room and return to the kitchen. "There's no more waiting."

Enid looks as if she's about to say something else, but she just works her jaw and keeps quiet.

I dial 911. The call connects almost immediately. "I need an ambulance. And the police," I tell the operator. "There's a dead woman in my kitchen."

I give her the address and hang up. I can't imagine it'll be long.

When I've set the phone down, I turn to my mother. There are a thousand things I want to say to her, but the only one that bubbles up is, "I'm sorry about the mess."

Her lips curl into a smile. Not a wide one, but one I know means she understands what I'm trying to say. "You have nothing to be sorry for. You saved my life. Again."

I want to tell her she's the one who saved *my* life, in all the ways that matter, but I can't speak over the lump in my throat. And then I remember Enid. I'm going to have to tell the police about Heath, about his involvement with Taylor.

When I turn to Enid, I find her crouched down over Taylor's body. As I watch, she pulls Taylor's phone out of the pocket of her jeans and taps at the screen.

"What are you doing?"

She looks up, startled. "I'm trying to cover for you. Obviously."

"What are you talking about?"

She rolls her eyes. "You think Sam wasn't smart enough to keep incriminating texts on her phone? Or something worse? We need to look through it and delete everything before the cops get here. Damn... it's got a passcode."

"Of course it does." No way would someone like Taylor leave anything wide open like that. "Let me see it."

I stare at the lock screen for a minute. I might not understand the inner workings of Taylor's mind — what would drive someone to the lengths she's gone to — but in some ways, I know her better than anyone else in the world.

After all, she *is* my half sister.

I take a deep breath and key in my father's birthdate. The phone unlocks.

I scroll through the home screen first, but there's nothing out of the ordinary — I recognize all the usual social media apps, Uber, Tinder, a few games, something called SelfieTune.

"Here, let me look." Enid reaches for the phone, and I instinctively move it out of her way.

Something nags at me. Something Enid said. But it's just out of reach, like a stray dog desperate for scraps but too timid to come forward. "Why are you so interested in this?"

"I'm trying to protect you." Her expression is pained. Desperate.

"Are you?"

"Alice, how can you even ask that?"

It hits me... Enid called her *Sam*. Not Taylor, which is the name I've been using. But Sam.

"How'd you know her real name?"

"Sorry?"

"Taylor. You called her Sam. How'd you know that was her actual name?"

"You must have said so."

"I didn't, though. I called her Taylor."

Enid's flustered. "I don't know. Maybe Heath said something."

"Right." I turn the idea around in my mind. Heath told me he never said anything to Enid — but if he was working with Sam, if they really were in on this together, he could have lied to me.

Or... Enid could be the one who's lying.

A heavy sense of dread fills my stomach as I click open Taylor's text messages.

Directly at the top of the message history is a back and forth with someone named 'E.' I don't have time to click it open before Enid grabs the phone from me, but I manage to read the most recent message, from 'E' to Sam.

E: This isn't what we talked about!

Enid has the phone now, and she's scrolling through it frantically. Tapping the screen. Deleting things, I'm sure.

"That was you, wasn't it? What did you mean — 'this isn't what we talked about'?"

Enid doesn't answer.

"Enid! What did you do?"

When she finally looks up at me, her face has changed. Her pupils are dark, her lips an unsmiling line.

"You've never really seen me, have you?" she sneers.

"What are you talking about?"

"All this time, living right next door to me, and you still don't really know me."

"Of course I know you. You're Enid. You're my—" I was about to say best friend, but this doesn't seem like the right time to blow smoke up her ass. "You're my friend."

"*Enid.* Good old Enid, right? Always there... when you have nothing better to do."

"That's not true."

"No? How many times have you bailed on me, just in the last couple of weeks?"

I don't have an answer to that because she's right. I'd been so enamored with Taylor that I'd been shitty to Enid. But that's not enough to justify any of this.

"How'd you even know Sam?"

Enid shrugs. "I met her through the podcast. She was a fan — she emailed me one day. We got to talking. She thought it was shameful how you treated me. That's the word she used, too. *Shameful.* She said you deserved to pay." Enid looks smug.

I feel sick. To think of Enid and Sam conspiring against me like that...

"You set up all of it? You let me get raped?"

Enid looks uncomfortable. "That was Sam's idea. She said you'd probably quit your job if that happened. You'd need someone to take care of you. To be there for you."

I have no words. "And killing Weston? Framing me for it? If I ended up in prison, I wouldn't be able to see you."

"That was Sam's idea, too. After the... first thing didn't

work. I would visit you, you know. In prison. I would have come every week, or as often as they let me. We would have so much time to get close."

From the corner of my eye, I see my mother shudder. I know how she feels. Twenty-five years I've lived next door to Enid. Twenty-five years I've been her friend. I never saw this side of her. I never even suspected it.

"So Heath had nothing to do with any of this? He wasn't dating Sam?"

"Heath? God, no. But that's another thing. How do you think it made me feel when you were in trouble and you turned to him instead of me? Don't you know I'd do anything for you?"

"It was you who called the police, wasn't it? Who told them where I was staying? How'd you know?"

"You can thank Heath for that. I saw the keychain for that dive you were staying at — the Sunset Motel. It had your room number on it and everything. One anonymous tip was all it took. The second time was harder; I didn't know exactly where you were staying, but I looked up the phone number you called me from and saw it was a gas station in Queens. I figured you had to be staying somewhere near there, so I looked up all the local motels and called the tip line with a couple that I thought were likely."

"Let me guess — that was Sam's idea, too?"

Enid looks uncomfortable. "It was her idea... but she was doing it to help me."

I laugh. "Sam didn't do anything for anyone else. She did all of that for herself."

"That's not true." Enid juts her chin out. "She wanted to

help me. She thought I deserved better. She told me so."

"She was working you, Enid. Sorry to tell you. Samantha Dennings was my half sister. She hated me because she thought my father chose me over her. She used you to find out what she needed to destroy me."

"No." Enid's voice drops to a whisper. "No, she wanted me to see that I deserved more. That's what she said."

"She said a lot of things," I say bitterly. "And she could be very convincing. You fell for her lies just like I did. So at least we have that in common."

Enid staggers forward. "No. You're lying. You never believed me. You never saw what I was capable of. You never even saw..."

Something in her voice stirs my nerves up again. "What do you mean, Enid? What didn't I see?"

"Nothing." She looks away. Her pale skin is even paler than usual.

I take two steps forward, closing the distance between us. My hands are on her shoulders, shaking her. "Enid. Tell me."

"Your father," she sobs. "What I did for you. I killed him for you, Alice. So he wouldn't hurt you anymore. So you and your mom wouldn't have to move away."

Her confession sucks all the air out of the room, out of my lungs. I hear the same whoosh of breathlessness come from my mother. For a moment, time ticks by impossibly slowly. Enid's confession hangs in the space between us, a suspended filmy soap bubble.

And then it pops. Enid lunges for the knife on the floor — the one Taylor had threatened me with a few minutes earlier. I lunge for Enid, trying to wrestle her away from the weapon.

My mother screams, tries to pull her off me. Enid slashes wildly with the knife.

"Mom, get back," I yell.

I try to pin Enid's arms to her sides, but she's wily and fast. She swings the knife again, catching my collarbone and dragging the point of the blade lower, toward the center of my chest. A white-hot pain staggers me, but I don't stop. I grab her forearm and push it away from me, try to walk her back toward the counter.

I slip. My sneaker slides through a trail of Taylor's blood and I fall against Enid. I don't let go of her arm, though, and then the two of us are tumbling to the ground. Blood is sticky against my face, but I don't know if it's Taylor's or mine or Enid's. All I can focus on is keeping that knife away from me.

Distantly, I hear the front door open. The police. Thank God.

"Alice? Enid? What the hell is going on?"

It isn't the police. It's Heath.

"Heath, help!" Enid cries. "Alice is crazy! She killed that girl and now she's trying to kill me!"

Jesus. I wrestle Enid's arm away from my face and try to catch Heath's eye. "She's lying. She was in on it the whole time. She set me up. Her and Sam."

Heath stands there, confused. He looks back and forth between me and Enid. His sister. His flesh and blood.

And he chooses me.

He grabs Enid by the arm, the one that's holding the knife, and yanks her to her feet. He throws her up against the counter, pinning her there.

"Drop the knife, Enid."

"Heath, you don't—"

"I said, drop the knife."

There's a beat of silence and Enid lets go. The blade clatters as it hits the floor. I kick it across the room, under the table.

With Enid restrained, the first thing I do is go to my mother. I'm expecting her to be completely losing her mind, but she's steady and composed. She's got the phone and she's narrating the events to the person on the other line — she's called 911 again.

"They're two minutes out," she says. "Keep her restrained until they get here."

"No problem," Heath answers.

All the fight's gone out of Enid. She's slumped against the counter. Her face is flushed, her cheeks streaked with tears. Red hair escapes her neat braid, sticks to her wet cheeks, her neck.

I look at her and try to see the Enid I've known for twenty-five years. It's impossible. All I can see now is the obsession. The madness.

I turn away. I turn my back on Taylor's body sprawled on the floor, on Heath standing guard over his sister, on my mother speaking confidently into the phone. Out the back window, I see the getaway tree that has always been my escape route.

But there's no more escaping. No more running. When the police arrive at the door, I greet them face to face and tell them everything.

FIFTY-ONE

One Year Later

I PUSH the spreadsheet toward her. "The numbers are all right here. Using Wilson's to bring in our deliveries will save money. Even though their prices are higher, the consolidated delivery fees will save us more than ten percent, or roughly eighteen thousand dollars a year. Same ingredients, better service, cheaper cost. It's a win-win."

Lola Hardwick eyes the columns of numbers I've toted up. "This is great, Alice. Fantastic."

I sit back behind my desk, pleased. Lola's office is still as dim and depressing as it was the first time I visited, but it's definitely more crowded now that it has two desks.

Lola had reached out to me after the whole story with Sam Dennings became public. She wanted to apologize for trying to turn me in to the police, but I told her no apology was necessary. I didn't blame Lola for what she'd done. Sam was clever, and she'd done a good job of setting me up to look guilty.

Lola understood that better than anyone. We'd gotten together over drinks at El Diablo one evening, and she told me all about how Sam had embezzled thousands of dollars from her. She wanted to go to the police, until Sam showed her pictures she'd taken. Photos that showed rats crawling through Frosting Queen's kitchens, cockroaches in the display cabinets. All photos Sam had staged, of course, but which she threatened to send to all the New York food bloggers and restaurant reviewers she could find. Lola's hands had been tied, just how Sam wanted it.

Lola and I had become friends from there, and shortly after, she offered me a job. I'd lost my job at Donna's Diner after I stopped showing up, and Lola took pity on me. Unfortunately, I was just as rubbish behind the counter at Frosting Queen. Customer service is never going to be my strong suit. But it turns out I'm a whiz with numbers and I have an excellent eye for inefficiency.

"Why don't you take the rest of the afternoon off?" Lola offers. "Spend some quality time with that handsome man of yours."

"Heath's working." I grin. "But I'll gladly take you up on that, anyway."

I depart Frosting Queen and head for the ferry. The air is chilly, and I burrow down deeper into my coat. On the ferry, I make a call.

When I step back onto land on Staten Island, I breathe out a sigh of relief. I love Manhattan, but for the first time in my life, I truly think of the island as home.

I stroll along the waterfront until I find our bench. I sit and wait.

My mother comes along shortly. She looks older now — her skin is more aged, her eyes more creased — but in every other way, she's younger and more vibrant than I've ever seen her. Other than some lingering pain in the wrist that Sam broke, the incident a year ago seems to have freed her. It's like something's been cleansed from inside her. A darkness that had been festering for far too long.

"Hi, sweetie." She sits next to me and pats my hand. "How was work?"

"Great. Are we still on for dinner Sunday?"

"Of course."

To anyone passing by, our conversation is benign, bordering on boring. But to me, it's nothing short of a miracle. My mother sold the house a couple of months after the attack and now lives in an apartment a ten-minute walk from mine. She does her own cooking, her own grocery shopping. She plays bridge. She has an entire life now, instead of that hobbled thing she used to have.

And she's not the only one. I share an apartment with Heath now, and although it's nothing fancy, it has a bedroom that's just ours, a kitchen table where we eat breakfast together every day, a balcony where Heath is growing a few small potted plants. We might even get a cat.

It had taken a while, but I eventually got back the money

Sam Dennings stole from me. And although it would have been nice to splash out on a nicer apartment or maybe a car, in the end, I decided to donate it to a non-profit that assists victims of sexual assault, the way I'd originally planned. Our tiny little apartment is enough for now, and I feel better knowing the money is going to help other people who've been through what I have.

"A year tomorrow," I muse, after a few minutes of silence.

"Are you okay?"

I shrug. "Fine." I think. Sam Dennings is never far from my mind. I've never stabbed anyone before and I hope I never do again. But there's a certain satisfaction in knowing I *could*. If I had to.

"Are you sure?"

"I got another letter from Enid the other day," I admit.

"What did it say?"

"I didn't read it." I smile. "I burned it. In the sink."

"Good for you. Maybe someday she'll stop writing to you."

"Probably not."

I don't know what triggered Enid's obsession with me, but it's still going strong. The letters come every week, like clockwork. I opened the first couple, but they were an unreadable mishmash of ranting diatribes, heartfelt pleas, and obsessive ramblings. They left me shook up and sad, so when Heath gently urged me to stop reading them, I listened. He's good for me that way.

Not that things between us have been easy. After all, his sister *did* try to kill me. But therapy is helping. We both go individually and together as a couple. Some people might say that a relationship that needs couples counseling to even get off the ground isn't worth pursuing, but I don't care what those people say. When it was all on the line, Heath was on my side. He believed in me. Trusted me. Fought for me. That's the kind of person I want in my life.

Enid might have killed for me, but it was never really *for me*. It was only to support her own sick fantasies.

"At least she's safely locked away," Mom says, tucking a strand of dark hair, streaked with grey, behind her ears.

"And she'll be there the rest of her life." Even though Enid hadn't killed Weston herself, she'd conspired with Sam to commit murder. Not to mention my rape. The judge was so disgusted with her that he'd given her life. And I don't feel a single bit bad about it.

But the truth? The deep down truth that I haven't even got around to telling my therapist yet? Sometimes I do feel a tiny bit bad for Sam. I'd envied Taylor when I first met her. Envied her for her ballsiness, her boldness, her freedom. But in the end, she'd suffered the same way I had — with a feeling that her life was shaped by the things that had happened to her, not by what she could do with the hand she'd been dealt.

"Walk me back to my apartment?" I say to my mother.

She hesitates. "There's something I want to tell you first."

My heart skips a beat. My mother's face looks so serious that I'm suddenly sure she's about to tell me something terrible. And I can't take any more terrible — not after the year we've had.

Mom takes a deep breath. "Ever since that whole thing with Enid, I've had this overwhelming feeling of guilt. My therapist thought it would be a good idea to talk to you about it. Get it out in the open."

My breathing regulates slightly. At least she isn't going to tell me that she has cancer, or something. "Tell me, then."

"I thought you were the one who killed your father."

"What?!"

She lowers her head. "I know. I'm so ashamed, to have thought such a thing about you. But I thought you were angry that he'd hit you, or afraid that I was going to make us move. I knew you overheard me on the phone with Barb, that I was thinking of taking you and heading for Colorado..."

My surprise turns into a sputtered laugh, which turns into me doubled over, laughing so hard my guts are about to burst.

"What's so funny?" Mom asks.

"I'm sorry," I pant. "I just..." I sit up, try to catch my breath. "I thought *you* killed him."

"What? How could you think—"

"The same way you thought I did?"

Mom's face softens into a smile. "I guess you're right. I guess we both had the wrong idea."

"We did. And I'm glad we at least know the truth now." I pause. "Is that why you were still so anxious after he died? Because you were worried about me?"

"I was anxious because I needed therapy. And meds. But yes, I suppose that was part of it. It felt as if things weren't over yet. That I was still waiting for the other shoe to drop."

I don't say anything. I suppose that's sort of how I felt, too. I really put my life on hold during the years after he was killed. I became a husk of the person I had once been, a closed-off hermit crab in a leather jacket shell. I didn't let anyone in, and I didn't let myself out.

The saga still isn't entirely over. Enid's case is still pending. But even if she's never convicted, she's in prison for life, and all the unanswered questions have been answered. The door is closed.

"I'm glad you told me," I say eventually. And I am. I'm glad I told her my own fear, too. It's good to have everything out in the open. No more secrets. No more fear.

We stand there in the crisp cool sunshine, looking out over the water.

Somewhere in the dark water is Enid's uncle's handgun. She threw it in there after she killed my father. That's what she told the police, anyway. They were never able to recover the gun.

But somehow, I know it's there.

I look out at the water again, imagining the gun rusting away under the dark, cold water. Then I slip my arm through my mother's, and we walk back toward my apartment.

Thank you for reading *A Friend Like That!* If you'd like be notified about upcoming releases, sales, and other special promotions, join Marissa Finch's mailing list. (Your info will never be shared.)

Sign up at http://eepurl.com/gRWUCj

If you enjoyed this book, please consider leaving a review

on Amazon or Goodreads, or simply telling your friends. Reviews and word-of-mouth recommendations are the best way to help readers find great new reads, and to support independently published books and the authors who write them.

ALSO BY MARISSA FINCH

Dirty Liar

Anything For You

ABOUT THE AUTHOR

Marissa Finch spent most of her life anxiously dwelling on worst case scenarios, so she decided to make a career out of writing those thoughts down and turning them into twisty page-turning fiction.

When she's not writing, she enjoys reading thrillers, watching crime dramas, cross stitching, and browsing Pinterest for pictures of haircuts. She lives in the country with her husband and two very entitled cats.

Printed in Great Britain
by Amazon

64490861R00227